WELSH WILDLIFE IN TRUST

Snowdon from the south across Afon Glaslyn

WELSH WILDLIFE
IN TRUST

Edited by

WILLIAM S. LACEY

PH.D. (Reading), D.SC. (Wales), F.L.S., F.G.S.

Reader in Botany in the University of Wales
Honorary General Secretary of the North Wales
Naturalists' Trust

Foreword by H.R.H. THE PRINCE OF WALES, K.G.

NORTH WALES NATURALISTS' TRUST,
BANGOR

Designed and Edited by W. S. Lacey.

Published by the North Wales Naturalists' Trust, Llys Gwynedd,
Ffordd Gwynedd, Bangor, Caernarvonshire, on behalf of all the
Naturalists' Trusts in Wales.

June 1970

Kite cover design by C. F. Tunnicliffe, R.A.

Printed in 11 point Caledonia, one point leaded, on Grosvenor Litho,
by Gee & Son, Denbigh.

Mountains, and woods, and the winds that blow over them;
Meadows, and downs, and the wild flowers that cover them;
Rocks, and ravines, and the mosses that smother them;
    All these I love with a love that possesseth me.

Sea, and the shore, and the shells the gods squander there;
Corals, and pools, and wild things that wander there;
Silence, and caves, and the thoughts that men ponder there;
    All these I love with a love that enchanteth me.

ANON.

The wildlife of today is not ours to dispose of as we please; we have it in trust and must account for it to those who come after.

KING GEORGE VI

CONTENTS

ILLUSTRATIONS

This book is a particularly appropriate one for European Conservation Year and contains articles written by many Welsh naturalists, some of whom belong to my Countryside in 1970 Committee for Wales. The title of the book is wonderfully apt since it should remind us that one of our duties on this earth is to hold what we have inherited in trust for future generations.

This applies to every sort of thing, but especially at this point in time and in this year it holds for our wildlife and natural resources. We are no more free now to do what we like with the wildlife of Wales than before. What we have got to try to do is reconcile necessary human progress with the survival of our wildlife. This is certainly not easy, but it is not beyond our capabilities. The articles in this book illustrate just how much we have to lose in Wales if, unlike the Naturalists' Trusts, we do not pay attention to our wildlife. One way to help solve this problem is to choose a voluntary organisation from the list of contributors to this book and join it.

Charles

Inch-perfect: a red kite having its beak measured before being released at a secret location in Scotland this weekend

Return of the kites

By Adam Fresco

THE Royal Society for the Protection of Birds has reintroduced red kites into Scotland for the first time since they became extinct during the last century. The 20 young birds were brought from Sweden in a joint operation between the RSPB and the Joint Nature Conservation Committee.

All the birds had radio tags fitted to their tails yesterday so that the RSPB can monitor their movements following their release over the weekend at a secret location in Scotland.

The red kites were abundant in the last century in Scotland and England, but were persecuted to extinction and now breed only in Wales. The birds have spent six weeks in quarantine since arriving in this country.

WELSH WILDLIFE IN TRUST

EDITOR'S PREFACE

In 1968 RAWDON GOODIER, then Regional Officer for the Nature Conservancy in North Wales, suggested to me that the Trust Journal *Nature in Wales* should carry a special article on 'Snowdonia' to mark European Conservation Year. I took this idea to the Editorial Committee and it was accepted, but as the Journal is currently produced by the collaboration of four of the six Naturalists' Trusts in Wales and also deals with natural history in the whole of Wales, it was felt that the scope of the article should be widened to include contributions from other parts of the country. It was decided therefore to publish a special additional issue of *Nature in Wales* for this purpose and I was asked to edit it.

After agreeing to undertake this task, I invited all six of the Naturalists' Trusts in Wales to participate in its production and I also approached a number of other organizations and individuals with requests for articles on their own particular conservation interests. The response was overwhelming. What was originally intended to be an " article " and then a " special issue " soon became a separate book in its own right and in the event I have been compelled to make the present selection from twenty-eight articles offered in order to keep it to a reasonable size and to avoid duplication of material.

The choice of topics is mine therefore. It has been made with two objects in view: to give a balanced presentation of as many natural history interests as possible within the compass of a small book; and at the same time to give an idea of what has been done, is being done and still needs to be done to care for the countryside of Wales and its wildlife.

The scope of the book is wide. It includes topics as diverse as the fascinating biographical account of the arduous 70-years-long struggle to preserve the kite as a breeding bird in Wales and the account of the practical steps being taken now to preserve rare plants on Craig Breidden threatened with extinction by quarrying; or as different as the description of the rich wildlife of Towyn Burrows (an invaluable record in view of the possible environmental changes which may take place if a Ministry of Defence Experimental Artillery Range is established there) and the short factual accounts of the work of the various conservation organizations in Wales.

In short, the book provides a wealth of information on the wildlife of Wales, presented, as is fitting in European Conservation Year, from a conservation point of view. It is hoped that it will appeal to the general reader and will also be of value to education authorities, teachers, planners and all those whose duties or interests necessitate consideration of the various aspects of land-use in Wales.

Individual contributors have been free to write in their own styles. I have introduced a measure of uniformity in the citing of common and scientific names of plants and animals by adopting the practice used in the *Journal of Ecology* and *Journal of Animal Ecology*. Some contributors have not used the scientific names of the wildlife they describe. Readers who wish to know them will be able to find what they require in the Index, where they are listed after the common names.

I have also endeavoured to maintain a high standard of accuracy but neither I as Editor nor the North Wales Naturalists' Trust as Publisher can accept responsibility for the statements and opinions of the contributors.

ACKNOWLEDGEMENTS

The publication of a book of this kind is made possible only by the willing help of many collaborators. In addition to the twenty-four writers of articles, who made my task relatively easy by submitting their original typescripts and returning their corrected proofs in good time, a number of other organizations and individuals, whose names would not otherwise appear, deserve special mention.

Particular thanks are due to Charles F. Tunnicliffe and Mary Grierson for readily agreeing to my request to prepare drawings specially for this book.

I wish to thank also the owners of the copyrights of the photographs used in the Plates for permission to reproduce them.

The very useful Map provided at the back of the book is the work of the Nature Conservancy, aided by the Countryside Commission.

I acknowledge with gratitude much editorial help from my colleague Mrs M. J. Morgan, M.Sc., F.R.E.S. at times when I was overwhelmed with other work, as well as the preparation of the Index and assistance with the proof-reading.

Finally, on behalf of all the Naturalists' Trusts in Wales, I record thanks and appreciation to the County Councils and individual well-wishers who made donations towards the cost of publication. Lists of organizations and individuals who have helped in various ways are given separately at the end of the book.

WILLIAM S. LACEY

Bangor.
April 1970

INTRODUCTION: THE ENVIRONMENTS OF WALES AND THE NEED FOR THEIR CONSERVATION

R. GOODIER, B.SC., *Nature Conservancy* and W. S. LACEY, D.SC., *North Wales Naturalists' Trust*

THE LAND OF WALES includes some of the most varied and beautiful scenery to be found anywhere in Britain, ranging from a coastline one thousand miles in length and of infinite diversity to mountain crags and summits of stark grandeur.

Translated into more scientific terms this means that the country provides many different kinds of ' environment', a word used in many senses, but for the biologist meaning the totality of the surroundings of living organisms. This is the way the word is used by ecologists, the natural historians of environment, and in this book also it is used in this sense, while at the same time recognising that the environments described are also the environments of man in Wales. These environments have both influenced his activities and been moulded by them and are as much to be cherished as any other aspect of his heritage.

THE PAST TO THE PRESENT

It is not possible to understand the present landscape in Wales without knowing something of its geological history. The rocks which form the physical basis of the land find their origin in the earlier periods of the earth's history. The oldest in Wales are the hard Pre-Cambrian rocks occurring in Anglesey and the north coastal parts of Caernarvonshire. Built up against these are the slow-weathering slates and grits of the Cambrian and Ordovician ages, accompanied by much contemporaneous volcanic activity, which form the mountain masses of Snowdonia in Caernarvonshire and of the Harlech Dome and Cader Idris areas of Merionethshire. Eastwards into Denbighshire and southwards into Montgomeryshire, Radnorshire and Cardiganshire softer Silurian mudstones, shales and slates ensue, yielding a more gentle rounded topography. Passing further eastwards still younger Carboniferous limestones and Coal Measures occur in Flintshire and Denbighshire, while in the south the much larger fragmented Carboniferous coal basin, spread over parts of Pembrokeshire, Carmarthenshire, Glamorganshire and Monmouthshire, is flanked by Old Red sandstone strata especially well seen in Breconshire. The youngest solid rocks of Wales are found only in the Vale of Clwyd in the north (Triassic sandstones), and in the Vale of Glamorgan in the south (Triassic sandstones and Liassic shales and limestones).

The biological components of the environment have a relatively recent origin, for the ice sheets cwm and valley glaciers formed in Wales during the Pleistocene Ice Age so substantially modified the landscape that, for most purposes, the evolution of the present biological environments in Wales dates from the final retreat of the ice about ten thousand years ago.

A study of the pollen remains found in lake deposits and in peat has provided evidence for the whole sequence of environmental changes since the Ice Age. At first the areas of bare ground left by glacial processes became colonised by plants characteristic of 'tundra' conditions, including the dwarf birch *(Betula nana)*, which no longer occurs in Wales. Subsequently, with amelioration of climate, trees began to spread into Wales, first birch and juniper *(Juniperus communis)*, then oak *(Quercus* species) until, at between about 5000 and 3000 B.C., the period of the most favourable climate since the Ice Age, most of Wales became tree-covered up to a height of about 2000 feet on the mountains. The subsequent history has been one of slight climatic deterioration accompanied by the increasing impact of man on the environment, leading to almost complete deforestation, a trend only recently reversed by man's own tree planting activities.

These major environmental changes have been accompanied by great changes in the distribution and numbers of different plants and animals found in Wales. It is against this dynamic background that the present-day environments of Wales must be understood.

For descriptive purposes modern Wales may be divided into four zones, a narrow coastal zone where the predominating influences are the physical and climatic processes associated with proximity to the sea; a zone consisting of the agricultural lowland and the foothills which were once largely forest-covered; a mountain zone, lying above the natural limits of tree growth and now largely used for sheep grazing; and the industrial zones, mainly in the south-east and north-east (Figure 1). The first three of these zones are the most important for the conservation of existing wildlife and are discussed here. Some of the special problems of the industrial zones are considered in the concluding sections of this book (Sections XX, XXI).

ENVIRONMENTS OF THE COASTAL ZONE

Although proximity to the sea has a fundamental effect on all Wales in providing the general climatic condition of high rainfall, cool summers and mild winters often referred to as an 'atlantic' climate, the more immediate effects of the sea in producing characteristic coastal environments are limited to a relatively narrow zone extending from the low tide mark up to one or two miles inland.

Between the tide marks the influence of the sea is immediate and overriding. Here the main distinction between the different types of environment relate to variations in the physical nature of the shore, or, in estuaries, the salinity of the water and here processes relating to shore erosion and accretion are most active. Within the tidal zone the major environments are distinguished as the rocky shore, shingle beach, the sandy shore, mud flats and estuary. Each of these has its characteristic community of animals and plants and, although there are some local variations in species represented, on the whole these communities are characterised by their distinctness and uniformity around the coasts. Each of these intertidal communities is biologically rich, containing a wide variety of species and often immense number of individuals, closely adapted to their physical environment and constantly replenished by the passage of the tides.

FIGURE 1. Semi-diagrammatic sketch showing (a) the coastal zone, (b) the lowland agricultural zone, (c) the mountain zone and (d) an industrial zone.

3

Above the mean high-tide mark the marine environments pass into the maritime, where the influence of the sea is still strong but not overriding. Here the erosion and accretion processes are still important so that, as in the case of the sand dune areas, the physical nature of the landscape may undergo rapid change. The animals and plants of maritime areas usually have a tolerance of wind and of salt spray, but because of the limitation on tree growth imposed by these factors many growth-forms occur which are adapted to 'open' non-wooded environments that were elsewhere extinguished by the development of the forests. Within the maritime zone the main distinct environments are those of the sand dunes (as, for example, Towyn Burrows, described in Section XIX, *p.* 136), the saltmarsh, the sea cliff and exposed cliff top. Each of these has its characteristic community of animals and plants closely adapted to the physical nature of the land. The off-shore islands of Wales (described by R. M. Lockley, Section XII, *p.* 80) also fall within this environment and are worth special mention because of their importance to nature conservation, though for the most part their interest is related to their sea cliff and exposed cliff top habitats.

There are many reasons why coastal habitats should be conserved. Apart from the scientific interest that derives from the ecological diversity and dynamism of coastal habitats, the interface between land and sea represented by maritime habitats is of particular significance for those large numbers of animals which live largely on the products of the sea but return to land to breed. Thus many sea birds are largely dependent for their survival on relatively small undisturbed breeding grounds and are particularly susceptible to reduction or extinction due to interference with their breeding habitat. Recent years have seen the severe impact of coastal oil pollution when it occurs near these breeding areas. Estuarine systems are particularly rich biologically, gaining nutrients both from the inflowing fresh water and from the tidal flow. They thus are able to sustain large numbers of sand or mud dwelling animals which are in turn fed upon by a rich and varied bird fauna. Here again the benefits which may be gained by commercial use of estuaries for water storage and/or recreation may have to be balanced against a loss of biological variety. Man has long been attracted to coastal areas for his recreation and this demand poses both problems and opportunities. In the long run the variety of characteristic habitats will be recognised as a source of much enjoyment; in the short term the fragility of these environments requires careful planning of recreational use so as not to destroy these basic assets. These problems are discussed by E. I. S. Rees and P. Hope Jones in Section XIII, *p.* 90.

ENVIRONMENTS OF THE LOWLAND AGRICULTURAL ZONE

It is within the zone once covered by woodland that man has made his biggest impact on the face of Wales. Beginning in pre-Roman times and continuing with increasing rapidity down to the Middle Ages, the woodlands were destroyed to provide timber for building and metal smelting and to give place for grazing-land for goats, cattle and sheep. With the reduction of the woodland many of the associated animals, such as the wolf, the boar and the deer, disappeared. Although much wildlife remains within the agricultural land, particularly in the hedgerows which still survive in Wales, and more recently in the environments provided by the increasing commercial afforestation (see Section IX, Forestry and Wildlife in Wales, *p.* 46) conservation in this zone has been largely focussed on three habitats, the small patches of relict deciduous woodland, the localised 'fen' or 'mire' communities, and the lakes and rivers.

The remains of the once extensive deciduous woodland, largely dominated by the sessile oak, but with birch, ash *(Fraxinus excelsior)* and alder *(Alnus glutinosa)* locally important, are now largely confined by man's activities to land unsuitable for agriculture. Thus small patches are found in inaccessible ravines or on rocky slopes as, for example, in Coedydd Maentwrog in Merionethshire. Occasionally these patches were augmented by planting, mainly during the last century. Most of these woodlands have been heavily grazed by sheep for decades and few contain many trees less than 100 years old. In spite of the grazing many of these woodlands have an interesting associated flora, particularly in the case of the western oak woodlands, of mosses and liverworts with very restricted distribution in Britain, and a fauna including characteristic species such as the pied flycatcher and, very locally in mid-Wales, the red kite (the subject of a special contribution by Col. Morrey Salmon, Section XI, *p.* 67).

The small lowland fens and mires are of a greater importance than their size would suggest as they are the remains of once far more extensive wetland communities which existed within the original forest cover and which have now largely been reclaimed for agricultural purposes by drainage. Because of their high, but fluctuating water levels and the inflow of mineral nutrients from surrounding lands they are often complex biological systems containing a great diversity of plants and animals and their isolation within the agricultural system has tended to make them important reservoirs for lowland wildlife. Cors Goch and Cors Erddreiniog in Anglesey and Cors Fochno and Cors Tregaron in Cardiganshire provide good examples.

The same considerations largely apply to the lakes and rivers within the lowland environment as these also frequently play the part of wildlife reservoirs. They share with the mires and to a rather lesser extent with the woodlands the problem of being greatly subject to the influence of surrounding land-use practices. Thus both mire and freshwater systems are vulnerable to contamination by agricultural fertilisers, herbicides and insecticides; their role as wildlife reservoirs may be easily detrimentally affected. The future of deciduous woodland fragments lying outside Nature Reserves remains problematical. They have little or no economic significance, yet they will require active management if they are to continue to contribute to the scenery and wildlife conservation as at present. In some cases fencing against grazing animals will be sufficient to allow regeneration, but in others more active steps such as tree planting may be required. Perhaps in the longer term the scenic and recreational value of these non-commercial woodlands will be realised so that wider re-creation of this interesting environment will be embarked upon. The part played by the National Trust in this connection is dicussed by H. J. D. Tetley, Section V, *p.* 24.

ENVIRONMENTS IN THE MOUNTAIN ZONE

Above about 2000 ft. on the mountains of Wales lies the zone in which man's influence has been relatively less important than elsewhere. Here the changes since the Ice Age have been more subtle and depend largely on the inter-relation between rainfall, soils, the vegetation and the grazing animals. The main distinctive types of environment are the heaths, the grasslands, the tundra-like communities of the mountain top and the steep rocky cliffs and gullies.

Mountain heath communities, dominated by heather *(Calluna vulgaris)* or bilberry *(Vaccinium myrtillus)*, are relatively scarce in Wales, largely because of the effect of sheep-grazing which in many areas has converted heather or bilberry moor into grassland in which these species play only a subordinate role. However, these communities are often found where the sheep-grazing pressure is relatively low because of the high altitude or because the terrain is too rocky to sustain high sheep numbers. Thus fine mountain heaths are found on the Black Mountains in Radnorshire and on the Rhinog Mountains in Merionethshire.

Grasslands are the most widespread of the mountain environments of Wales and they cover many thousands of acres. The main types are those dominated by the purple moor-grass *(Molinia caerulea)* occurring on thin peats characteristic of the Central Wales plateau and those with sheep's fescue *(Festuca ovina)* and mat grass *(Nardus*

6

stricta) on the mineral soils of Snowdonia. Locally, in Snowdonia and elsewhere, sheep's fescue and bent *(Agrostis)* grasslands with a larger number of associated herbs occur on better quality soils derived from relatively lime-rich volcanic rocks. These can sometimes sustain up to three times as many sheep to the acre as the surrounding poorer mat grass-fescue grasslands.

As well as providing valuable grazing, the mountain heaths and grasslands, together with the rough grazing areas, with the agricultural zone below them, form the chief recreational environment of upland Wales. Here occur the unenclosed mountain vistas and the freedom to walk unimpeded in wild country.

The environments of the mountain cliffs are of special interest and importance because their inaccessibility has made them refuges for many plant species which cannot withstand grazing on the higher mountain slopes. These include species, such as the moss campion *(Silene acaulis)* and purple saxifrage *(Saxifraga oppositifolia)*, which have survived in these places since the end of the Ice Age. Because of the discontinuity of the habitat these plants occur on mountains in a number of scattered localities in Wales ranging from Snowdonia southward to Brecon Beacons. The contributions by M. Porter on Breconshire (Section X, *p.* 54) and by C. A. Sinker on Breidden Hill, Montgomeryshire (Section XVIII, *p.* 129) refer to some of these interesting plants.

The windswept tundra-like vegetation of some of the high peaks and summit plateaux of Wales, where frost action and erosion ensure instability of the environment, similarly represents a continuity of type with that prevailing at the end of the Ice Age. This is again apparent from the flora which may contain plants such as the dwarf willow *(Salix herbacea)*, reindeer moss *(Cladonia rangiferina,* a lichen) and also many 'Arctic-alpine' insect species which are confined to mountain tops in Britain.

Both the inland cliff and mountain-top environments occupy very small areas of land in Wales, of little or no economic value for agricultural purposes. Some of them are used for recreation and in some instances, for example where rock climbers remove vegetation to facilitate their sport, or buildings and paths are sited on sensitive summit areas, there is a danger that some of the great interest they contain may be lost. The problems of footpaths and conservation are discussed by Professor P. W. Richards in Section VIII *p.* 41.

PROSPECT

During the past twenty years nearly 100 Nature Reserves have been established in Wales by the Nature Conservancy and the Naturalists' Trusts. These have generally been chosen as the best examples of the more natural types of environment to be found in Wales and serve both as 'living museums', yardsticks by which other environments can be measured, and as outdoor laboratories in which environmental processes can be studied. More need to be established if examples of the full range of environments are to be conserved.

Environments are dynamic systems; even those relatively little influenced by man are changing gradually in adaptation to climatic changes and physical changes in the landscape. As they are also very complex systems it is unlikely that all that is going on within them will ever be known and management of environments for the purposes of conservation must inevitably be a fairly crude process, aimed at satisfying certain principal aims. What sort of aims might these be?

Perhaps first of all environments should be managed so as to leave future freedom of choice to the present generation and to posterity. As far as possible, practices which lead to environmental processes which are very difficult to reverse should be avoided. Secondly, variety should be retained from which alternative environmental balances appropriate to future needs can be chosen. Thirdly, as far as possible, examples of those aspects of the environment which illustrate its history should be preserved — sometimes this will be difficult, particularly where they depend on types of land-use which are no longer economic. Finally, attempts should be made to contribute something positive appropriate to our own day and age which results in enhancement of the environment. The Lower Swansea Valley Project (Section XXI, p. 151) is an outstanding example of such an endeavour.

II

A SHORT HISTORY OF THE NATURALISTS' TRUST MOVEMENT IN WALES

DILLWYN MILES

West Wales Naturalists' Trust

" MAKE CONTACT with your local Naturalists' Trust — they are the front-line troops in the battle for the countryside. . . . We've got to act while there is still some time, and time is running out ". This was the advice given by the Duke of Edinburgh when asked how one could help in the conservation of nature.

'Your local Naturalists' Trust' is a voluntary body which aims to secure and protect — while there is still time — places of natural beauty and of special interest as habitats of animals and plants, so that the heritage we now enjoy shall survive for future generations. It promotes and encourages study and research in the natural sciences and provides an opportunity for people to become involved in the conservation of the environment.

The first Trust was established in Norfolk in 1926, but it took another twenty years for the next to be set up, in Yorkshire in 1946, and yet another fifteen years before the first Trusts were formed in Wales. There were, nonetheless, bodies that were active in conservation, like the West Wales Field Society which was a Trust in all but name from its formation in 1945 and which Max Nicholson used to describe as " in effect the second Trust to be founded in Britain ".

The WEST WALES NATURALISTS' TRUST had its origins in the Pembrokeshire Bird Protection Society which was established in 1938 by L. D. Whitehead, then owner of Ramsey, and R. M. Lockley who at that time lived on Skokholm, and Lord Merthyr, in collaboration with the Royal Society for the Protection of Birds. From the outset it received representations from the adjoining counties to extend its boundaries but, owing to the outbreak of war, was not able to do so until July 1945 when the West Wales Field Society was formed.

From its inception the Pembrokeshire Bird Protection Society wardened Grassholm and had oversight of Skokholm and Skomer;

and of Ramsey from 1942. It obtained a lease of Cardigan Island in 1944.

In 1946 the newly-formed West Wales Field Society purchased Dale Fort which it leased to the Council for the Promotion of Field Studies for the purpose of establishing its first Field Centre. In 1949 it set up a Kite Preservation Committee and in the following year took over the management of the Orielton Duck Decoy. In that same year it obtained a 21-year lease on St. Margaret's Island.

In 1953 its plan to promote a " Nature Reserves Society for Wales " was deferred when the Nature Conservancy set up its Committee for Wales. It helped to establish the Bardsey Island Bird Observatory and the Lleyn Ornithological and Natural History Society. In 1958 it purchased Skomer for £10 000 and re-sold it to the Nature Conservancy by agreement, whereby it was declared a National Nature Reserve and leased to the Trust.

The first steps towards the transformation of the Society into a Naturalists' Trust were taken in 1959 but legal formalities delayed its incorporation until 1961.

The Trust has over 1200 members and has sections at Haverfordwest, Tenby, Newport, Aberystwyth, Dolgellau and Carmarthen and it has established Reserve Committees in each of the four counties. It has also set up an Education Panel in an effort to promote an understanding of the countryside by establishing educational nature trails and investigating other educational processes.

The Trust has acquired, by purchase or by lease, over 20 nature reserves covering 1,500 acres. It shares responsibility for West Orielton Lake and Decoy with the Field Studies Council, has the care of Craig yr Aderyn in Merioneth and wardens Grassholm on behalf of the R.S.P.B. It has established over twenty hedgerow reserves in West Wales and four nature trails, including a ' model ' educational nature trail.

In 1955 it published the first issue of the journal *Nature in Wales*, as a quarterly until 1961 and bi-annually thereafter. In 1963 it invited other Trusts to adopt *Nature in Wales* so that it would become the journal of all Naturalists' Trusts in Wales and the invitation was accepted by the North Wales Trust in 1964, and later by the Brecknock Trust and by the Radnorshire members of the Herefordshire and Radnorshire Trust. Its other publications include *A Guidebook and Self-Guiding Trail to Skomer Island, The Birds of Pembrokeshire, The Birds of Cardiganshire, The Birds of Carmarthenshire, A Contribution to the Flora of Merioneth, A List of Flowering Plants and Ferns of Carmarthenshire, The Plants of Pembrokeshire,* and a *Handbook of Nature Reserves in West Wales.*

The GLAMORGAN COUNTY NATURALISTS' TRUST was formed, under the guidance of H. J. Hambury, Neville Douglas-Jones, Colonel H. Morrey Salmon and Christopher Methuen-Campbell at an inaugural meeting held in January 1961 and it was incorporated in the following May, thus being the first Trust to be officially established in Wales. From the commencement it set up a West Glamorgan Section, based on Swansea, and an East Glamorgan Section centred on Cardiff, but in 1968 its increased membership called for branches to be formed at Merthyr Tydfil and at Bridgend and further branches will be set up when membership will justify doing so. At the end of 1969, the Trust had close on 1000 members.

The Trust owns or leases, or has rights over twenty-three nature reserves, twenty of which are described in the informative *Handbook of Nature Reserves* published by the Trust in 1969. The first to be acquired, in May 1962, was the Broad Pool, Cilibion, in the centre of the Gower Peninsula. After this, an eyesore of less than half an acre in Mayals in the town of Swansea was cleaned up and planted with trees and shrubs among which nest boxes were erected so as to provide a sanctuary for birds in an increasingly built-up area. Eight more reserves were acquired between 1964 and 1967, including a 'hanging-wood' at Cwm Ivy, Port Eynon Point and Overton Cliffs acquired in collaboration with the Gower Society and the National Trust, and Melin Llan Wood used jointly with the Welsh Scout Council. In 1968, ten further reserves were acquired, including quarries, cliffs, wood-lands, mountain-land, a reservoir and a canal. Another three reserves were established in 1969, at Ogmore Down, Berry Wood at Gower and Peel Wood at Oystermouth. There is a nature trail at Port Eynon Point.

The Trust produces an annual *Bulletin* and its publications include *Reserves in Gower, Wild Orchids of Gower* and *A New Nature Reserve: Glamorgan Canal* (Dr Mary E. Gillham).

The proposal to establish the NORTH WALES NATURALISTS' TRUST was made in January 1963, with the encouragement of the Nature Conservancy and the Society for the Promotion of Nature Reserves (Section IV, *p.* 22). The initial meeting was held under the chairman-ship of Professor P. W. Richards, Professor of Botany at the University College of North Wales, Bangor, and at that time Chairman of the Conservancy's Committee for Wales. The prime movers were Dr W. S. Lacey, of the Botany Department, who had been impressed by the activities of the Yorkshire Naturalists' Trust when he visited York in 1959, and who was appointed Honorary Secretary, Mr R. H. Roberts, who became Hon. Deputy Secretary and Colonel J. C. Wynne Finch, who has been President from the outset.

The Trust was formally established at a meeting held at Bangor in October 1963, which was addressed by Lord Hurcomb, Christopher Cadbury, James Fisher and Clough Williams-Ellis.

The local circumstance leading to the formation of the Trust was the need to conserve Cors Goch, an area of more than 100 acres of rich fen, limestone scarp, grassland and heath near Benllech, which had come on the market in 1961 and was being held by the Society for the Promotion of Nature Reserves: this was eventually purchased for £3400 in 1964. In the same year, the Trust received 30 acres of land at Morfa Bychan, near Portmadoc, as a deed of gift and acquired 10 acres of Cilygroeslwyd Wood, in Denbighshire, for a nominal sum. Coedydd Maentwrog, a woodland of about 180 acres, was purchased jointly by the National Trust and the North Wales Trust for £10 000 and leased to the Nature Conservancy as a National Nature Reserve. Eight other reserves have been established in various parts of North Wales.

The Trust has over 1000 members and it has branches in the Conway Valley, in the Clwyd Valley and in Montgomeryshire. An Anglesey Branch is in the course of formation. In 1967 the Trust helped to establish the North Wales Conservation Corps (see Section VII, p. 34).

It issues a *Newsletter* three times a year and an illustrated *Annual Report;* it was largely responsible for the subject matter in the *Natural History of Anglesey,* published by the Anglesey Antiquarian Society in 1968.

The BRECKNOCK COUNTY NATURALISTS' TRUST was established at a meeting held at Brecon in January 1964, and was incorporated in the October following. The first steps towards its foundation were taken in June 1963, by some members of the Council for the Protection of Rural Wales who circularized a number of people in the county. Its sponsors included Major-General Sir Geoffrey Raikes, Dr David Kyle, the Rev. J. Jones-Davies and Mr J. O. Evans, who became its first Honorary Secretary.

The Trust has Botanical, Geological and Ornithological sections, and arranges regular field meetings and monthly indoor meetings. It has a membership of 360.

Nature reserves have been established on land acquired by lease at Tŷ Mawr Pool, Llanfyrnach and at Craig y Rhiwarth, near Craig-y-nos, which was acquired by agreement. The Trust is investigating the acquisition of a number of other sites, including two stretches of a disused railway line, and plans to set up hedgerow reserves. A nature trail is being planned at Priory Groves, Brecon, in conjunction with the Brecon Borough Council.

The Trust produces a *Newsletter* every six months and publishes *Breconshire Birds* annually.

The HEREFORDSHIRE AND RADNORSHIRE NATURE TRUST was one of the many that came into being as a result of the re-activation of the Society for the Promotion of Nature Reserves. It was established in November 1962, with the aid of the Rural Community Councils in the two counties, which continue to provide the secretariat. The Lords Lieutenant of the two counties are the joint Presidents of the Trust and there is close co-operation throughout.

The Trust supervises the sites of special scientific interest listed in the two counties for the Nature Conservancy, and sites of botanical and ornithological interest by arrangement with the Forestry Commission. One of these is the blackcock reserve in Marteg forest, the Barns and Blue Links area of which extends into Radnorshire.

In 1968 the Trust was able to acquire Titley Pool in Herefordshire as a nature reserve and wildfowl refuge at a cost of £2000 with the assistance of a grant of £250 made by the Radnorshire County Council from the Welsh Church Fund.

The Trust has 350 members, many of whom have been actively concerned in schemes for the conservation of the badger, the placing of a thousand nesting boxes in 35 woodlands, protecting doomed wild daffodils by transplantation and organising butterfly breeding schemes for schools.

The Trust issues a *Newsletter* twice a year and its Radnorshire members co-operate in the publication of *Nature in Wales*.

The MONMOUTHSHIRE NATURALISTS' TRUST was established as a result of the activities of a group of business men, lecturers, teachers and naturalists aided by the Monmouthshire Rural Community Council. An inaugural meeting was held in 1963 and the Trust was incorporated the following year. By the end of 1969 the membership of the Trust was 360. Trust members have addressed various organisations in the county on conservation matters and a close liaison is maintained with local authorities and interested voluntary bodies.

During the first year of its existence, the Trust succeeded in obtaining a woodland reserve by agreement with the owner at Llanishen, near Chepstow. At the same time it commenced negotiations to lease land at Magor and now manages some sixty acres of bog on peat as a nature reserve. By arrangement with the Cwmbran Urban District Council, the Trust has obtained the use of a stretch of the Newport-Pontypool Canal for educational work and it has also managed to establish a wildfowl refuge at Peterstone by agreement with the Usk River Authority, the Eagle Star Insurance Company and the Wildfowlers' Association. At Cleddon Woods, near Llandogo, the

Trust manages a woodland reserve, consisting mainly of beeches, on the side of the Wye Valley.

At the request of the Trust, the Monmouthshire County Council declared the famous Trellech Bog, the only lowland acid bog in the county, a Local Nature Reserve.

The Trust publishes a quarterly journal, *Monmouthshire Newsreel,* and it issues the *Monmouthshire Wildlife Report* annually.

Within a decade the whole of Wales has been covered by Naturalists' Trusts. They have a total membership of 4250 and between them they have acquired almost as many acres of land which they manage as nature reserves. This is a remarkable growth of interest in the conservation of the environment, but it must be remembered that the membership constitutes only an infinitesimal portion of the population of Wales. These are ' the front-line troops ' and they need considerable reinforcements in the form of new members before ' the battle for the countryside ' can be won, ' while there is still some time — and time is running out '.

III

THE R.S.P.B. IN WALES

JOHN CRUDASS

Reserves Manager, Royal Society for the Protection of Birds

THE HISTORY of bird conservation in Wales by the Royal Society for the Protection of Birds has meant, over the years, facing up to diverse and continually increasing threats and challenges. Some of these are age-old and have remained virtually unchanged; others have increased in scale and intensity; yet others are completely new.

For many years country people have been painfully aware of piece-meal and largely unplanned encroachment by urban expansion. The tempo has increased and with an expanding population continues to do so. To a great extent we are now an urban population and large areas of the countryside have disappeared beneath bricks and mortar. Habitats have gone, never to return; what is left is under heavy and increasing pressure from an urban population which becomes more and more mobile and which progressively needs more land for, amongst other things, production of food, roads and recreational purposes.

Residents on the coast of Wales are ever conscious of the horrors of oil pollution but this is not a new problem; they might be surprised to learn that as far back as 1931 the Society initiated a successful prosecution against the National Benzole Company for an incident off Skokholm Island. At that time tankers were small, the majority of ships were coal burning and an incident might involve a few hundred tons of oil; we now think in terms of hundreds of thousands of tons and the statistical possibility of another occurrence increases daily; the evil remains but the scale has increased to a frightening extent.

As long ago as 1925 the Society was paying honoraria to voluntary watchers to protect the birds of the Pembrokeshire coast from shooting and other forms of disturbance, and continued to do so until 1938 when it was closely involved in the formation of the Pembrokeshire Bird Protection Society, which, as already described more fully by Dillwyn Miles, became the West Wales Field Society and later still the West Wales Naturalists' Trust. After 1938 financial support was given to the new local Society which organised this protective work. One of the species then most threatened by egg collectors, falconers and shooters was the peregrine and the voluntary watchers were particularly charged with its care. That the threat to the few pairs of this species left in South Wales remains is shown by the necessity, in 1969, for local ornithologists with the support of the R.S.P.B. Technical Officer, to organise a watch to safeguard a threatened eyrie. Egg collecting has certainly decreased but still continues. Much of the activity is the result of thoughtless action by young people and in this direction the educational work of the Young Ornithologists' Club is having a considerable effect. The Society co-operates with responsible falconers who are well aware of the importance of maintaining a viable population of raptors but the irresponsible elements remain and protection is needed. In pre-war days shooting was largely the hobby of the more well-to-do but the importation of low-priced, easily-obtained shot-guns from the Continent has changed the picture considerably. 'Marsh Cowboy' activities are a constant and squalid nuisance calling for continual action by the Society and its local members. New protective measures have had their effect to an extent but each new law by its very nature creates new offences and there follow quite naturally new methods of circumvention, in turn calling for increased vigilance. Under the terms of the Society's Charter it is not permitted to enter into discussion or arguments on the ethics of shooting but this does not prevent friendly co-operation with the Wildfowlers' Association of Great Britain and Ireland, a body which has done a great deal to educate the less responsible 'sportsmen' as well as carry out practical conservation.

Perhaps, however, the most insidious and far-reaching development has been in the field of agricultural chemicals. Pesticides and herbicides have transformed standards of living in many countries, and this is to their credit, but they have brought enormous problems and have confronted conservationists with a dilemma not yet wholly resolved. Working in co-operation with the British Trust for Ornithology and the Game Research Association, the Society has focussed the attention of the public and the authorities on the dangers inherent in the continued uncontrolled use of these substances and this resulted in the adoption of a voluntary system of control. There can be no doubt that the use of persistent organochlorine substances has seriously effected the breeding capacity of many species including, particularly, the predators who operate at the upper end of the food chain. Included in this category in Wales are the kite, peregrine and buzzard, birds which have faced attack on more than one front and certainly in the case of the first two have only with difficulty maintained a precarious hold. The full story of kite protection is recounted by Col. Morrey Salmon (Section XI, *p.* ??). The recent heavy mortality of seabirds on the Welsh, Scottish and Irish coasts has brought to the fore yet another threat, that of the danger of industrial waste containing poisonous chemicals. Appreciation of the scale and extent of the disaster resulted from information supplied by participants in the Society's Beached Birds Survey which has operated for thirty years. Examination of bodies produced for analysis proved the presence of polychlorinated biphenyls, substances used in various manufacturing processes and persistent organochlorines. Whilst it cannot be said that these substances were the direct cause of the deaths of these seabirds, the possibility cannot be ruled out.

Another relatively new, but increasingly common threat is now to be faced — photography. This in itself is not new but the easy availability of cheap complex photographic equipment is, and this has resulted in an enormous increase in the number of amateur exponents whose effect on wildlife, especially birds, in their continual quest for closer 'close-ups' can be very serious. Many of these people are ignorant of the implications of disturbance either in its effect on the bird or the fact that it is an offence under the law. Whether or not the law is broken, a disturbed bird very often means a failed nest and at that stage no amount of legislation can effect a remedy.

In countering these and many other threats the Society has taken practical steps, the results of which are clear to see. Its advice is sought almost automatically by planning authorities in various parts of the country. It is involved at international level with the prevention of pollution by oil and at national level with the mitigation of its effects. Money is paid out in the form of rewards to those who protect nests of certain species of raptor. Over a period of years it has been involved particularly in assessing the effects of pesticides on birds, but also in the wider field of environmental pollution and it is involved in the initiation and preparation of legislation.

There are however, other more positive fields in which it is closely involved and at least two of these are worthy of fuller consideration, affecting as they do the work of the Society in Wales.

As one of its main practical supports to conservation the Society has purchased or otherwise acquired a number of reserve areas throughout Britain. These are acquired for a variety of reasons: the protection of a particular, possibly declining species; the maintenance of a fast-disappearing type of ornithological habitat; the development of land with the aim of attracting species or, in rare cases, the protection of a long lost but newly-returned species. In Wales the process of reserve acquisition started many years ago with the purchase in 1948 of Grassholm Island, famous for its colony of gannets. The management of Grassholm has not always been easy or straight-forward. In 1945, for instance, the Society found it necessary to intercede with the Air Ministry who were using the island as a bombing range. Their very firm representations resulted in an undertaking from the then Under Secretary at the Air Ministry that the island would not again be used for this purpose. Over the intervening years the gannetry has increased in size and numbers; one of the contributory factors may well be the almost impossible landing conditions which have virtually stopped visiting. The island has been managed for the Society by the West Wales Naturalists' Trust since its purchase. Ramsey Island, with which the Society was involved as long ago as 1937 at the time of the negotiations leading to the formation of the Pembrokeshire Bird Protection Society, has, with the agreement of the late owner Mr K. P. Allpress, and more recently Mrs Allpress, been under its management for a number of years. A formal, longer term agreement is now in course of preparation. A detailed account of these Island Reserves is provided by R. M. Lockley (Section XII, *p.* 80).

This reserve acquisition policy has recently been intensified in Wales with the purchase of the Gwenffrwd reserve in the Upper Towy Valley near Rhandirmwyn and a second reserve, Ynyshir, on the Dovey Estuary. These were purchased with money collected in the recent Reserves Appeal which raised over £100 000. Both have resident wardens, John Humphrey at Gwenffrwd and William Condry at Ynyshir. Apart from acquisition for reasons already stated, Reserves also fulfil other functions; for instance as laboratories for ecological research or reservoirs in which wildlife populations can replenish themselves. The use of a reserve area as a research laboratory need not necessarily imply work by advanced students but can equally apply to simple work done by school children.

It is the Society's view that education is the foundation on which conservation must be based; reliance on statutory control to preserve the countryside and its wildlife is basically a negative attitude; genuine concern by the individual must be the motivating force. The older age groups have not by any means been left out, for the emphasis on articles directed towards education in the magazine *Birds* is aimed at this group, as also are reserve visiting, lectures and film shows, but the young are the main target. Controlled visiting on reserves is permitted and the educational use for organised parties arranged through the local or education authorities is being developed and increased. In this way an understanding of the countryside and its problems will be instilled in the young for the benefit of future generations. The process is slow and much time, money and effort will be needed.

The reader will by now be aware of the type and variety of work the Society has undertaken in Wales, although this article merely

PLATE 1: *Above*, the Conway valley looking north: afforestation on the eastern edge of the Carneddau to the left and on the Denbighshire moors in the foreground and to the right. The Rhyd-y-Creuau Field Centre lies on the eastern side of the valley in the middle distance. *Below*, the Brecon Beacons, with Ty-mawr pool, the Brecknock County Naturalists' Trust's first Nature Reserve, in the foreground.

touches the fringes of it. He may not have any knowledge of the Society's history and constitution — knowledge which is essential if he is to consider giving his support.

Towards the end of the nineteenth century a group of ladies, mainly from what was described then as the 'upper classes', formed a committee to combat the importation and use of plumes in the fashion trade. Egrets, herons, birds of paradise and other species with attractive feathers were in many cases seriously depleted and in some almost exterminated to satisfy the demand. In 1889 the committee constituted itself in Didsbury, Manchester, the 'Society for the Protection of Birds'. The 'subscription' was 2d. per annum for a membership card inscribed with the rules, associates were enrolled for the minimum annual payment of 1/- and life members paid one guinea. By 1897 the Society had a London address and a Secretary was employed; 1901 saw the appointment of the first watcher, to protect pintail on Loch Leven, and in 1904 a Royal Charter was granted. An early essay into the educational field — interesting in view of the recent emphasis in this direction — was the 'Bird and Tree Competition' for schools.

In 1904, as a result of pressure by the Society, the poletrap was declared illegal; it is sad to report its continuing use throughout the country; 1908 saw the first legislation resulting from the Society's activities being presented but, because of strong opposition and later the World War, the Importation of Plumage (Prohibition) Bill was not enacted. Thus the original object in founding the Society was not achieved until 1921 with the enactment of a bill banning plumage importation, but in fact, because of a Government Order in 1917, no imports had occurred since that date. In 1931 the first Sanctuary on Romney Marsh was purchased but sold shortly afterwards when drainage rendered it useless for its original purpose. Eastwood, Stalybridge by bequest, and part of Dungeness by gift, came into possession in the same year and both remain in ownership. During the intervening years the Society has grown year by year almost without check, except during the war years, and the scope and scale of work has also multiplied. More reserves, now 36, covering about 14 000 acres, more responsibilities resulting from an increasing and very mobile population, and more legislation, amongst other things, have called for a larger staff to cover such activities as education, publications, sales, protection, publicity, films, etc. — the list is almost endless. 1969 saw the enrolment of the fifty-thousandth member, whilst the Young Ornithologists' Club for people under seventeen stands at over 22 000. The headquarter's staff numbers sixty-five (an additional thirty are taken on to cope with the Christmas sales rush), Scottish office — four, and Northern Ireland —

two. External staff, including representatives and wardens, number nineteen in permanent employment, with a further ten during the breeding season. Annual income from sales and membership investment runs at about £175 000, which may seem a large figure but is in fact inadequate to meet the demands being made. Higher membership is essential and the recent increase — over 10 000 in 1969 — goes part of the way towards meeting the deficit.

The Society is not merely a protesting body, although it will not hesitate to protest should the occasion demand, but a forward-looking organisation intent on using its resources and influence to nurture an appreciation of the countryside and to care 'for birds and their place in nature', the charge laid upon it by Royal Charter.

What of the Society's future in Wales? The acquisition of suitable reserve areas will continue either by purchase, lease or management agreement. In this way birds and their environments can be protected to some degree but it should be emphasized again and again that, with an awareness on the part of the public, reserves would become largely unnecessary. Such an ideal situation must be the aim, however distant, of a progressive body in which education is one of the main goals. A new concept in this field is the plan to set up 'nature centres'. Such centres, to which school parties will be invited, will include lecture, display, projection and other facilities and will be situated either on or near a reserve area on which a nature trail can be laid out. Access will be arranged through the local education authority and the programme of instruction integrated with the school curriculum. In this way the nature centre becomes an integral part of the country's education system. A pilot scheme has been operating at The Lodge, Sandy, Bedfordshire during 1969 when on three days each week visits have been made by school parties. Instruction is given by the staff, both full and part-time, of our education department, assisted by the reserve warden. School teachers accompany the parties for disciplinary reasons — they take no part in the instruction given. They are encouraged to take advantage of the interest aroused and to develop it by taking and using a 'follow-up' kit which includes ideas for simple projects. That the experiment has been a success is proved by the number of school visitors, over 4000, and by the distances which some parties have travelled; a round trip of 100 miles is not unusual. It is intended that when resources allow such a centre will be set up in Wales.

The Society will continue to look to the enforcement of legislation affecting egg collecting, nest robbing, illegal shooting and any other activities detrimental to birds; it will also continue to press for additional legislation where it is considered necessary. The growth of the Society and the increase in its activities inevitably and properly

20

mean decentralisation. This is not a new development, as the formation of the Pembrokeshire Bird Protection Society showed; the process continues and a Welsh Committee is now being set up. Its function, broadly speaking, will be to advise the R.S.P.B. governing body, Council, on matters relative to bird protection and conservation in Wales. It is also hoped, when finances permit, to open a Welsh office with a resident representative who will supervise all aspects of the work in the country.

IV

THE NATURALISTS' TRUSTS AND THE SOCIETY FOR THE PROMOTION OF NATURE RESERVES

W. H. F. DAWSON

Assistant Secretary, S.P.N.R.

ALTHOUGH THE STRENGTH of the voluntary nature conservation trusts is attributable to their local appeal, the spread and success of the movement and its co-ordination at national level owes much to their association through the Society for the Promotion of Nature Reserves, an organization set up in 1912 with the original aim of protecting British wildlife, both at home and overseas, by establishing Nature Reserves.

It was in 1958 that the S.P.N.R. established its County Naturalists' Trusts' Committee, at the request of the six Trusts then in existence, to provide a forum for the exchange of ideas and information, the means of representing their common interests and negotiating with national bodies, and the opportunities for securing grants and loans from national sources. From this small beginning of six Trusts, with fewer than 2000 members, the Committee was able to promote and assist in the establishment of new Trusts so that the whole of England, Scotland and Wales was covered within six years. As 1970 begins there are thirty-eight Trusts with a total membership of some 42 000. They own, lease or manage by agreement, some 450 Nature Reserves covering nearly 40 000 acres and are involved in many other conservation and educational projects.

The Society for the Promotion of Nature Reserves is now the National Association of the Conservation and Naturalists' Trusts, continuing and expanding the original purposes of the County Trusts' Committee through which all Trusts are represented. The Society has established a full-time secretariat to service the Association and specialist committees have been set up to advise on publicity and administration and on technical conservation. The latter, the Conservation Liaison Committee, includes representatives of the major voluntary organizations concerned with conservation management and is recognized as the liaison committee between them and the Nature

Conservancy on technical conservation problems. Liaison is also maintained with the Nature Conservancy on policy matters, and with the Royal Society for the Protection of Birds, the National Trust, Countryside Commission, Forestry Commission and other national organizations. The Trusts are represented on the Council for Nature through the Society, which helps to support the Council financially and administratively.

The S.P.N.R. has been notably successful in attracting financial aid for the Trusts from charitable foundations. Through the generosity of the Pilgrim and Nuffield Trusts, grant and loan funds have been established by the Society to assist Trusts to purchase properties suitable for management as Nature Reserves. Since 1963 more than £12 000 in grants and £70 000 in interest-free loans have been made available to Trusts from these funds to help to purchase properties costing some £200 000. These include a good number in Wales. S.P.N.R. has also financially assisted the National Trust in Wales Section V, p. 24). More recently, the Society has been able to persuade the Carnegie United Kingdom Trust to set aside a fund of £30 000 to assist the Trusts in employing administrative and conservation staff and in promoting educational projects such as field museums. Two Welsh Trusts are already benefiting from this fund; the North Wales Naturalists' Trust has just appointed its Executive Officer (March 1970).

The Society's other services to Trusts include the production of sales items such as Christmas cards, which benefited Trusts by some £7000 in 1969; the production of publicity material such as a common National Cover Brochure and posters; the publications of standard schemes for biological recording and a policy on introductions to nature reserves; the compilation of articles and news abouts Trusts for journals and the Press; and the provision of an information service to Trusts.

The Trusts' association as a nation-wide voluntary conservation movement was further strengthened by the Society in 1969 when it proposed that all members of Trusts should be elected Associates of the S.P.N.R. It is hoped in 1970 to introduce a periodic publication of conservation news for all these associate members and to publish a Handbook of Nature Reserves, showing which may be visited by reciprocal arrangements among Trusts.

V

CO-OPERATION WITH THE NATIONAL TRUST

H. J. D. TETLEY

National Trust and *North Wales Naturalists' Trust*

IN ADDITION to its basic function to care for and protect houses and countryside "of Historic Interest or Natural Beauty" the National Trust has a clause written into the National Trust Act of 1907, part of which reads as follows: —

"The National Trust shall be established for the purpose of promoting the permanent preservation for the benefit of the nation of lands and tenements . . . and as regards lands for the preservation (so far as practicable) of their natural aspect features and animal and plant life."

This last field has become of increasing importance and interest during the last twenty years and the Trust in its turn is increasingly realising its responsibility towards the wild life on its properties.

Over the years it has created and managed a number of nature reserves at Wicken Fen and Blakeney in Norfolk, the Farne Islands off the Northumberland coast and Strangford Lough, Belfast.

Recently, however, with the birth and growth of the Nature Conservancy and Naturalists' Trusts, there have come into being bodies whose ultimate interest and function is, to a far greater degree than the National Trust, concerned with the protection of our native wild life.

The National Trust is in a position, however, to provide an extremely wide variety of habitat from its properties and as these are predominantly in quiet areas of countryside there are bound to be a number which are ideally suited to preservation of wild life, with the added requirement for a reserve of national importance that they contain some unique or unusual natural feature meriting special protection.

In Wales, and particularly in North Wales, areas of this kind have been found within properties owned by the Trust more frequently than in many other parts of Britain.

At this point it should be stressed that the Trust has always considered that it has a responsibility to see that nothing is done to upset the balance of nature on its properties, subject to the necessity to accept contemporary changes in agriculture which are not fundamentally destructive. The provision of reserves, however, has only comparatively recently been felt to be necessary as pressures on wild creatures increase.

In Wales the first area to become a National Reserve was Cwm Idwal in Caernarvonshire in 1954. In this case the Trust was approached by the Nature Conservancy, which was anxious to protect the rare alpines to be found in this area. With the agreement of the agricultural tenants concerned, some 984 acres were surrendered from farm tenancies and leased to the Conservancy which agreed, however, to the grazing rights remaining with the farms concerned. Public access too was permitted to continue as it was not necessary to curtail it. Thus nobody suffered but the rare plants had their extra protection.

The second Reserve, named Coed y Ganllwyd, is an area of some fifty-eight acres of oak woodland near the village of Ganllwyd, about six miles north of Dolgellau in Merioneth. Here the Conservancy was particularly interested in the unusual variety of bryophytes which were to be found in the woodland with its continually moist atmosphere due to the local high rainfall and continuous spray from the waterfall, Rhaiadr Ddu. Here there was no difficulty with agricultural tenants, but fencing was needed to exclude sheep and allow natural regeneration in the woodland. The Conservancy agreed, however, to fix stiles and gates on all paths to allow public access to continue.

The third Reserve in North Wales is that known as Coedydd Maentwrog on the north side of the Vale of Ffestiniog on the hillside running east from the Oakeley Arms Hotel at Maentwrog, in Merioneth again.

The acquisition of this area of some 180 acres of ancient oak woodland was an excellent example of co-operation between different organisations to produce a successful result.

In the first instance the North Wales Naturalists' Trust had hopes of being able to acquire the area and launched a vigorous appeal which produced a substantial sum. This was insufficient to meet the whole purchase price and the National Trust was approached. The latter was able to find the balance required for the purchase, but in order to give maximum protection to the land made it a condition that it should hold the land and declare it inalienable. It was mutually agreed that the Nature Conservancy be asked to take a lease, as in previous instances, and to manage the property as a Reserve. This was satisfactorily settled and once again public access was accepted as part of the pattern.

The property was of particular interest because of the steadily diminishing areas of oak woodland in North Wales and the danger of losing the creatures which are associated with it. Its acquisition and proper management as a continuing oak woodland area preserve a habitat of value.

The North Wales Naturalists' Trust, the Nature Conservancy and the National Trust have a small management committee consisting of a representative of each organisation. This meets as and when required to consider points of management and to ensure that the interests of each organisation are borne in mind and catered for.

Finally, in Anglesey, at Cemlyn where the National Trust has recently acquired the Cemlyn Estate with its lagoon and wet land areas and its thirty years tradition as a bird sanctuary particularly for wildfowl in winter, there is a plan to lease about thirty acres of particular ornithological importance and interest to the North Wales Naturalists' Trust, which will manage them as a Wildlife Reserve.

Here again circumstances have fortunately enabled this to be done without interfering with the neighbouring agricultural interests of the remainder of the estate and without having to curtail access by the public to the areas most suitable for that purpose.

The Naturalists' Trust will take over responsibility for organising wardening and generally supervising projects for introducing the public to bird-watching and the ideas of conservation of wild life. The National Trust, as owners, will assist where it can but will safely leave to others the welfare of the wildfowl and other bird life which has been and remains such a feature of the property.

From the foregoing it will be seen that there are many different ways in which conservation organisations with varying loyalties can combine to achieve a single aim provided each will take its part, and in these times, when pressures are increasing and habitats are shrinking, so that it is vital for all bodies concerned with conservation to work closely togther, it is pleasant to be able to record that during the period that these arrangements have been in being there has been no serious argument or difference of opinion between those concerned.

In South Wales the National Trust was able through Enterprise Neptune, and with the aid of a temporary loan from the Society for the Promotion of Nature Reserves, to acquire the 670 acre Whiteford Burrows which is part of the Whiteford National Nature Reserve. It is a peninsula of sand dunes, salting and beaches and adjoins the proposed Burry Estuary National Wildfowl Refuge. The flora, particularly that of the dune slacks, is recognised as one of the most varied and interesting in the region. The invertebrate fauna is also highly distinctive. Whiteford is well known, too, as a feeding and resting place for wildfowl wintering in the Estuary. The whole Reserve Area is now run with the advice of a management committee comprising National Trust, Nature Conservancy and Glamorgan

County Naturalists' Trust representatives, who seek the advice of other interested bodies such as the Gower Ornithological Society and the West Glamorgan Wildfowlers' Association when appropriate and provide an excellent example of wide co-operation.

On a smaller, but no less important scale, the National Trust has leased about eight acres of woodlands at Llanmadoc and thirty-three acres of cliff land at Port Eynon Point to the Glamorgan County Naturalists' Trust. These areas were adjacent to existing Glamorgan County Naturalists' Trust reserves and are managed entirely by this body for the National Trust.

In Pembrokeshire it has recently leased to the West Wales Naturalists' Trust Marloes Mere, an unusual basin of marsh adjoining the cliffs on the south of the peninsula, with a mixture of bog, fen and intermediate communities which is, however, of greatest interest as a habitat for birds; and West Hook cliffs on the north side of the same peninsula, consisting of three-fifths of a mile of cliff habitat.

To conclude, the object in setting out this short tale of one small corner of the conservation story is to show the interlocking parts played by Naturalists' Trust, Nature Conservancy and National Trust in achieving at least a measurable contribution to the protection and preservation of wild life in one area of Britain. Undoubtedly the reason why it has been successful is because those who feel strongly that conservation is of immense importance in saving our natural heritage in these threatening times are generally prepared to give and take for the sake of a cause they feel to be paramount.

VI

EDUCATION AND THE COUNTRYSIDE

A. T. SAWYER, B.SC., M.I.BIOL.

Monmouthshire Naturalists' Trust

EARLIER THIS CENTURY it was not uncommon to find that East London children were unable to understand reading books which dealt with such things as grass and cows; they just did not know what a field of grass looked like and a cow must have seemed an improbable animal to them. Even now some children express surprise and sometimes disgust at discovering that the milk which comes to them in clean, sealed and sterilized bottles comes from farmyard beasts. Nowadays the ubiquitous motor car scuttling rapidly from base to destination and back again gives its occupants glimpses of the countryside, ensuring that most people are aware of grass, trees and farm livestock and television will have given a secondhand knowledge of the countryside to the diminishing few who never travel by car.

Although a very superficial knowledge of the countryside is now more widespread than some forty years ago a new ignorance of the detail is becoming all too common. Habits change and the child walking along lanes, across fields and through woods to school is now a rarity; children in country districts tend to be confined to the school bus as schools become larger and their catchment areas grow correspondingly greater. Lizards sunning themselves on fence posts and wall cannot be seen through the windows and the retiring woodland plants remain hidden a few yards from the bus. Not only are the children deprived visually, the scents and sounds of the countryside become lost to them as well, the rustling of the wren and the skylark's song are lost in the roar of the diesel engine and the rattle of the flexing motor body. Not only the children but also the adults are becoming insulated from their natural environment; the man living within walking distance of his employment is an increasing rarity and what is regarded as a reasonable walking distance is getting shorter and shorter; the ploughman no longer " homeward plods his weary way ". He does not even bicycle his way home. Someone walking is generally regarded as in need and many a kindly motorist will stop and offer a lift. A family walk on a Sunday is about as eccentric now as family prayers and bible readings. It is not surprising that young men and women choosing to study biological subjects at sixth form and even university level are sometimes unable to recognise an ash tree or even a buttercup flower.

The education services do not yet seem to be fully aware of the cultural deprivation following these recent changes in social habits. Very few schools make provision for *all* their pupils to go frequently into the countryside to become acquainted with what is there. Many of those teachers who recognise the problems find that attempts to organise visits into the neighbouring countryside fail at the administrative hurdles such as insurance for pupils, cost of transport, the problems of arranging access to woods, etc.; even the use of headed notepaper and who writes the necessary letter can provide difficulties. The most difficult hurdle to clear is the timetable operated within an institution, for in many schools the period of time for any particular class to meet is about forty minutes and for some subjects two forty minute periods, both far too short for a useful journey outside the school; a whole morning or afternoon is usually necessary and frequently a whole day. Obviously these minor difficulties are capable of solution if there is sufficient motivation on the part of the administrators. Ideally the motivation should come from the administrators, but in this far from ideal world pressure applied by parents, teachers, the inspectorate, and general public opinion can help to move the administrative machine.

The teachers most often wishing to go into the countryside are those teaching biological subjects. Often those much maligned men, the G.C.E. syllabus organisers, put practical work in the field into the biology syllabuses and emphasise its importance and sometimes even make it compulsory, as with the W.J.E.C., G.C.E. "A" Level Botany. In this subject an account of field work carried out by the candidate has to be submitted some months before the theory examination. For many years botanists and zoologists have recognised the need for students to watch live animals and plants in their natural surroundings and the separate study called ecology has grown up encompassing the inter-relationships between living organisms and their environments. Ecology is found on almost every syllabus at "O" and "A" Level G.C.E. A recent move has been to include animal behaviour in syllabuses; this very desirable addition is best studied in the field and no one who has watched robins defending their territories or male sticklebacks doing the same can fail to understand the roots of human territorial behaviour, nationalism, patriotism. The structuring of human societies may also be better understood if the peck order of birds has been watched in the field.

The Field Studies Council long ago recognised the need for places situated in biologically rich areas where students could study wild life and we have the Council to thank for the provision of the Dale Fort Field Centre, the Orielton Field Centre in Pembrokeshire and the Drapers' Field Centre near Betws-y-coed (Plates 1, 2). In England, but hardly at all in Wales, the torch has been taken up by the local authorities who are establishing their own field study centres, e.g., the Bradwell Field Studies and Sailing Centre in Essex. Kent has set up some day field centres in disused schools, e.g., Godmersham in the Stour Valley. An interesting example of local authority co-operation is the Gibraltar Point Field Studies Centre at Skegness in Lincolnshire where the local authority gives very substantial grants to the Lincolnshire Trust for Nature Conservation to run the centre and also pays for a Field Studies Tutor. This kind of co-operation could be very fruitful elsewhere since most of the expertise in wild life is found in the Naturalists' and Conservation Trusts but money available for educational purposes is best raised by a local rate. In Monmouthshire, which includes part of the Brecon Beacons and much of the Wye Valley, there is as yet no Field Study Centre at all but an attempt is being made to start a centre as a private venture. The Monmouthshire Naturalists' Trust provides a variety of habitats in its Wildlife Reserves for local schools, colleges and universities to use, but lack of finance so far prevents the provision of residential accommodation and laboratory facilities on site. The same remarks apply to the Welsh Trusts in general.

Interest in the countryside is not confined to biology teachers. The Field Studies Council provides facilities for artists who in the past have shown considerable interest in scenic beauty. The area around Flatford Mill has long inspired artists and so has the area around Betws-y-coed. Does the present concentration of artistic work in studios have anything to do with an educational system which favours an indoor approach? Would more contact with the countryside at early age stimulate the young artist's imagination? Student artists from the Newport College of Art have certainly found much of interest on the Monmouthshire Trust's Reserve at Magor. Geographers and geologists have always been interested in taking parties of students into the countryside. The Field Studies Council centre at Juniper Hall, Dorking, has long been used by such students. A most encouraging change has come over the school sports scene which used to be dominated by ball games and team games; now it is being realised that rock-climbing, boating and pony-trekking are very valuable in character training and in developing muscular co-ordination and strength. These 'newer' activities are more likely to be continued after the adolescent period than football and cricket. Many local authorities are providing residential facilities in Wales for these pastimes — most of them being English authorities — as, for example, Coventry's Plas Dol-y-moch Outdoor Pursuits Centre, near Maentwrog in Merionethshire, in which county is also found the Arthog Field Centre owned by the Shropshire local authority. Even apparently unlikely subjects can have a relationship with the countryside, such as woodwork classes making bird boxes and canoes. Mathematics too in mensuration and statistical studies can be related to the countryside.

The emotional response is one which tends to be overlooked in these increasingly matter-of-fact days. Sometimes it seems possible that scientists do not realise that the æsthetic pleasure from colours and shapes is often responsible for their choice of subjects. The flowers, butterflies, moths and birds, all with brilliant colourings, have always had a good following and there has always been interest in miniatures; hence the interest in the microscope and the formation of clubs and societies to look at the very small. Dr Desmond Morris's movement from the scientific world to the artistic world was interesting in this day and age and Peter Scott's ability to combine science with art is another reminder that the two subjects are not unconnected. A large number of poets have been sufficiently stirred to record their emotions in verse and many a scientist will feel a kinship with the poet Wordsworth writing of a butterfly

> ' I've watched you now for a full half hour
> Self-poised upon that yellow flower.'

or Walter de la Mare writing of a snowflake

> ' Beneath these ice-pure sepals lay
> A triplet of green-pencilled snow
> Which in the chill-aired gloom of day
> Stirred softly to and fro.'

All kinds of artifices are resorted to by teachers of English to stimulate their pupils to write with feeling; ' happenings ' are introduced. What better than the natural stimulus of beauty in the countryside?

The distinction between education and leisure activities is fast disappearing, especially for adults. Extra-Mural departments of universities and colleges find good audiences for ecological classes with an outdoor content. Those with a dislike of formal education often find that nature trails provide the answer. The Forestry Commission has organised such trails as, for example, Beddgelert Forest Trail and Gwydyr Forest Walks. The Nature Conservancy and Naturalists' Trusts in Wales have also organised many Nature Trails. Local authorities in Wales have not been very active in this field although guided walks have been arranged in the Brecon Beacons National Park and several schools in North Wales have organised their own Trails. Nature Trails have also been sponsored by Shell, the petrol and oil company, in co-operation with the National Trust and several Naturalists' Trusts, the pamphlets being printed at Shell's expense and distributed at their garages.

Many County Naturalists' Trusts attempt to interest and inform members of the general public in wild life matters by staging exhibitions and holding film evenings. The Monmouthshire Trust organised such an evening in 1969 in the Little Theatre in Newport at which a 'House full' notice had to be used, the audience being in excess of the seating capacity of over 400. Trust speakers also go into schools by request to talk to the children. Women's Institutes and clubs of all sorts invite speakers on wildlife and countryside matters. Natural history films made by industrial concerns and nationalised companies like the Transport Commission are in great demand.

Unfortunately there are negative aspects to the co-ordination of countryside and educational activities, but once these are recognised the worst effects can be mitigated. Paradoxically many of the harmful effects result from well-meaning activities. It is not unusual for teachers to ask children to bring in as many different types of wild flowers as possible and in the resulting collection rare plants are often to be found, sometimes unrecognised. The Cambridgeshire and Isle of Ely Education Committee in consultation with the local Naturalists' Trust published a booklet in which 250 flowers which could be picked were listed together with rare plants which should not be picked. This example has been followed by several Trusts and there are plans to publish a national booklet suitable for the whole country under the supervision of the Society for the Promotion of Nature Reserves. The collecting activities of museums can be a cause for concern and so also is the collecting of material for classes studying wildlife. The coastal area round the Plymouth Marine Biological Station, for example, is known to have become depleted over the years. These problems are discussed further in Section XIII, p. 90. Frogs are much rarer than they used to be and the collectors supplying schools have been blamed, although other factors may be responsible. Common flowers may be taken every year from the same area until they become quite rare. An Outdoor Studies Code giving guidance on this and other countryside matters has been printed and distributed by the co-operation of County Naturalists' Trusts, the Field Studies Council and the Nature Conservancy. Copies can be obtained from the County Trusts and the Field Studies Council; there should be a copy in every school and college.

Although the countryside needs to be looked after and protected, it also needs to be utilized to the full for the benefit of all. This needs money for the provision of car parks and toilets, money for residential centres that are not too spartan but not too expensive, money for the transport of children to the countryside, money for the establishment of information centres, informative leaflets and noticeboards, money for the organisation and co-ordination of countryside activities. The Countryside Commission is a first step in the national plan and the Countryside Committees of local authorities are taking their first steps at the county level. Some education authorities are taking steps to help, even to the extent of running in-service classes for teachers in wildlife matters, such as the one day course in ' Ornithology in the School' organised by Monmouthshire Education Committee. The machine has started to move, it must be kept moving; those authorities still static must be helped and encouraged and given the occasional push until all the parts are working in harmony and the long neglected countryside becomes a source of interest and pleasure to all.

VII

THE ROLE OF LOCAL WORKING PARTIES

R. G. GIBBS, B.A., PH.D.

North Wales Naturalists' Trust

IN THE EARLY DAYS of nature conservation in this country the general principles of reserve management were simple: a fence was placed round the reserve which was left to its own devices. The same applied to many other areas which were set aside for their scientific interest or for public recreation and education. However, it was soon found that unexpected changes took place inside the fence. Chalk grassland developed into scrub and then woodland when grazing animals were excluded, and this process was accelerated when rabbits were decimated by myxomatosis. If people were allowed inside the fence, marshy ground could be converted by trampling into a churned morass. Estuaries colonised by cord-grass *(Spartina townsendii)* no longer supported the same community of plants and animals, and ponds became choked with weed and gradually dried out.

It was eventually accepted that these areas require positive management if they are to retain their value. While some bodies can employ paid workers to carry out the management, many other organisations are dependent on voluntary labour, in which increasing numbers of people are involved. What attracts the volunteers? They come because they enjoy a certain amount of hard work in the open air, and because it allows them to see places in the countryside that they might not otherwise visit. In addition, they derive satisfaction from helping to do a job which needs to be done. Although the main purpose of running voluntary working parties is naturally to get the work done, such parties have a useful educational role and the opportunity is usually taken to interest the volunteers in the scientific and amenity importance of the area.

The parent body of the local volunteer groups is the Conservation Corps of the Council for Nature. The Corps was set up with the aid of a generous grant from the Carnegie United Kingdom Trust, and held its first working party on Box Hill in the North Downs in February 1959. Work undertaken over the years has included a large element of scrub clearance, the clearing of overgrown and silted-up

PLATE 2: *Above*, the Field Studies Council's Field Centre at Dale Fort, near Haverfordwest, Pembrokeshire. *Below*, members of the North Wales Conservation Corps repairing a footpath in the Cwm Idwal National Nature Reserve.

ponds and water-courses, tree-planting and the stabilisation of sand dunes with marram grass *(Ammophila arenaria)*. For the first few years the tasks were residential, lasting from one to two weeks in the Easter and Summer holidays, and most of the volunteers were students or school children. More recently weekend tasks have been run from London throughout the year. Not surprisingly, a considerable nucleus of enthusiastic and dedicated volunteers has been built up over the years. Most of the credit for this must go to the first organiser of the Conservation Corps, Brigadier E. F. E. Armstrong, who is now carrying out the same function for the Gloucestershire Trust for Nature Conservation. Although most of the tasks in the first few years were held on such well-known reserves as Wicken and Woodwalton Fens, Box Hill and Gibraltar Point, work is now carried out at a great variety of sites, including many county Naturalists' Trust reserves. Residential task sites in Wales have included Newborough Warren in Anglesey; Snowdon and nearby Cwm Idwal; Cilygroeslwyd Wood near Ruthin; the Dovey Estuary; and Whiteford Burrows in Gower.

Conservation Corps activities have recently been extended to include tasks on farmland as well as in nature reserves and public open spaces. This stems from the gradual realisation that wildlife cannot survive solely in nature reserves and that features of farmland such as hedgerows, banks and coppices provide important cover and food for plants and animals. This new aspect of the work of the Conservation Corps, known as 'Operation Habitat Rescue', is being carried out in co-operation with the Soil Association. The first tasks undertaken on farmland have included tree-felling and planting, cleaning out ditches and laying hedges. Surveys of wildlife to study the effects of such management are also being conducted.

One of the by-products of residential Conservation Corps work is that the volunteers, drawn from all over the country, may return home fired with enthusiasm to continue the work in their local area. This leads on occasion to the sorry picture of a lone figure, silhouetted against the setting sun, hacking away at the hawthorns on his local common, but more often such volunteers are absorbed into local groups. These usually come under the direction of the county Naturalists' Trust, but North Wales has its own independent local Conservation Corps, organising weekend tasks similar to those run from London. The organisers, Geoff Gibbs and John Sheldon (the latter replacing Alan Morton who was assistant organiser for three years), both work at the University College of North Wales, Bangor, and many of the volunteers are also students at the college. Tasks are held fortnightly on Sundays during term-time, with one full weekend task per term, usually to a more distant site. The two-day tasks, where the party stays overnight in a local youth hostel or outdoor centre, are popular and do much to improve the social structure of the Corps.

The majority of tasks undertaken so far have consisted of estate management work. Thus frequent parties have helped to keep fence lines clear on woodland reserves including those at Gorswen and Dolgarrog in the Conway Valley. The maintenance of clear fence lines, through the periodic removal of shrubby vegetation for a yard or so on each side of the fence, facilitates subsequent repair work as well as preventing rotting vegetation from causing the deterioration of the fence itself. A second task which, though physically hard, is popular with volunteers, is the maintenance of footpaths through reserves. Much work of this type has been carried out on Cwm Idwal National Nature Reserve (Plate 2), where the footpath leading from the A 5 at Ogwen Cottage past Llyn Idwal to the Idwal Slabs and Twll Du (the Devil's Kitchen) is heavily used by walkers and climbers. After wet weather the surface of the path becomes churned up and subsequent users tend to avoid the centre and walk on the edges of the path. This soon leads to the widening of the path and serious erosion can result. The process can be observed in a particularly advanced state on the lower stretches of the Pig Track on Snowdon. The solution is to provide proper drainage of the path by channels and culverts, to stabilise and mark out the edges of the path with large boulders and provide on the path itself a firm walking surface of gravel overlying hard-packed stones. The North Wales Conservation Corps has now spent five days working on the Cwm Idwal path under the guidance of Warren Martin, one of the Nature Conservancy wardens, and the results, together with those achieved by other volunteer parties, are now beginning to show. It should not be assumed, however, that the erosion of these mountain paths is now under control, as no serious attempt has been made to tackle the worst examples, namely those on Snowdon. Indeed, it is doubtful whether voluntary parties, as at present organised, are capable of dealing with these paths. Professor Richards discusses the whole question of footpaths and conservation in the following Section VIII.

The North Wales Conservation Corps has also been called upon to help with the construction of several nature trails. The most interesting of these is that on the long-established Precipice Walk on the Nannau Estate near Dolgellau. A number of different countryside organisations co-operated in helping to set up this trail. It was planned by the Snowdonia National Park Information Officer, Gwilym Rhys Edwards, with expert advice from Peter Hope Jones of the Nature Conservancy, and the manual work was carried out by the North Wales Conservation Corps. An enclosure for a demonstration plot of conifers was constructed and the trees subsequently planted, stiles and walls were repaired, and finally the posts for the various stations along the trail were erected. A second trail on which the Corps worked is at Coed Llyn Mair, part of the Coedydd Maentwrog N.N.R. in the Vale of Ffestiniog. This trail was designed to attract visitors alighting from the Ffestiniog narrow gauge railway at Tan-y-bwlch station and has in fact proved very popular in its first summer.

Not all the work of the North Wales Conservation Corps can be classified as estate management and much time is spent trying to preserve particular types of vegetation on reserves. Such tasks could be considered as 'habitat management' and those carried out in North Wales have largely consisted of removing unwanted types of vegetation. Thus rhododendrons (the naturalised *Rhododendron ponticum*) have been cleared from the more overgrown parts of oakwood reserves in the Vale of Ffestiniog and elsewhere (the cut stems being treated with a herbicide to prevent sprouting), encroaching scrub cut back on limestone glades in the North Wales Naturalists' Trust's Cilygroeslwyd reserve near Ruthin, and the first few clumps of colonising cordgrass *(Spartina)* dug up on the Braint Estuary, along one edge of the Newborough N.N.R. This last task is a perfect example of 'a stitch in time saves nine', as *Spartina* spreads very rapidly once it gets a hold. Many Welsh estuaries as, for example, the Dovey in mid-Wales and around the Gower peninsula in South Wales, could now be cleared of this unwanted plant only by extensive spraying with chemicals. Interestingly enough, attempted chemical control of *Spartina* on the Braint Estuary was not successful at the first attempt, and the Conservation Corps may well have to finish the job by hand.

The total number of man-days worked by the North Wales Conservation Corps in its first three years of existence (1967-69) was 624, of which 67% was on National Nature Reserves and 17% on North Wales Naturalists' Trust reserves. The National Nature Reserves attracted the majority of tasks for two main reasons. North Wales is particularly well endowed with them, and the Nature Conservancy is better equipped with ecologists to write management plans than with estate workers to execute them — hence the need for the Conservation Corps. Naturalists' Trusts, on the other hand, usually rely on scarce voluntary expertise to plan the management of their reserves, which thus tends to lag behind reserve acquisition. As time passes, the North Wales Conservation Corps will probably tend to work less for the Nature Conservancy and more for the North Wales Naturalists' Trust (as it gets its management plans written) and for other voluntary organisations. Indeed, this is one of the advantages of keeping a local Conservation group independent of any other body — the effort can be concentrated where the need is greatest. Working parties run directly under a Naturalists' Trust, on the other hand, will obviously have to do what the Trust decides, even if this means repeated visits to the same reserve carrying out the same task. Independent organisation means that a programme can be planned to contain a pleasant variety of tasks, which is more likely to sustain the interest of volunteers.

The cost of running an independent local group is low, largely because overnight accommodation is usually not required. Where accommodation is provided, volunteers pay ten shillings each towards the cost and the balance is paid by the body for whom the work is carried out, which also reimburses car owners who transport volunteers to the site. Private cars are the normal form of transport, but the Nature Conservancy sometimes provides a Land Rover for this purpose. The organiser's running costs, amounting to a few pounds per year, are met in the case of the North Wales Conservation Corps by the national Conservation Corps, which also provides insurance cover for those taking part in the tasks. Working tools have been provided both by the North Wales Naturalists' Trust and by the national Conservation Corps.

It should not be concluded from the account above that North Wales is unique in its voluntary conservation working parties. M. D. G. Powell, Conservation Officer of the Glamorgan County Naturalists' Trust, organises parties of members in West Glamorgan who so far have worked mainly at the Trust's Gellir Hir Wood, erecting nest-boxes and building hides overlooking the lake. He has also had valuable assistance from the Territorial Army and the Footpaths Group of the Gower Society. The latter helps by keeping footpaths clear in the Trust's reserves and with other maintenance work. As well as working on their own reserves, Mr. Powell's volunteers also co-operate with other organisations. At Whiteford Burrows, for example, they erected two hides which were provided by the Nature Conservancy, thus greatly improving the facilities for bird-watchers on the reserve. Further west still, the West Wales Naturalists' Trust is faced with its greatest management problems on the island of Skomer, off the Pembrokeshire coast. They were helped by City of London police cadets, who came for a number of years to maintain the quay, landing place and some buildings on the island. Local schoolchildren have also helped to clear bracken there.

All tasks discussed so far have been primarily concerned with nature conservation. It is very difficult, however, to draw a firm line between such tasks and similar work undertaken by other voluntary countryside organisations. Several International Voluntary Service groups have, for example, worked in the Caernarvonshire section of the Snowdonia National Park in the last few years, repairing the Snowdon Ranger path and other footpaths, collecting litter and repairing fences. Similar tasks have been carried out independently by the members of the Snowdonia National Park Society, whose main litter drive has taken place in the Sychnant Pass. Voluntary work has also been undertaken by school parties staying at Outdoor Pursuits Centres in the Merioneth section of the National Park, where they have come to be instructed in mountain walking, climbing and canoeing. Many of these activities take them onto upland sheep farms and some farmers have complained of straying stock and damage to fences, allegedly caused by these parties. Whatever the facts of the matter, some of these school parties now spend a day of their visit helping the farmers, for example, by carrying posts up to high mountain fences which are inaccessible by vehicle. This sort of co-operation and goodwill must lead to better understanding between residents in the area and those staying at the Centres.

A rather different kind of voluntary work is undertaken by groups of children in the Gower Peninsula. They attend a Crusader's Care of the Countryside course, which is run by Douglas Evans, warden of Gower A.O.N.B., and on completion are awarded a certificate. As part of the course the girls have to carry out tasks such as scrub clearance and litter picking, while the boys construct paths and perform other tasks. In addition they help to man a caravan to which visitors may come for information about routes, natural features and local history, and from which the Crusaders dispense first aid. This interesting scheme is sponsored by the Gower Commoners' Association and appeals mainly to the 12-16 year-old age group.

One pointer to the future of local Conservation Corps groups is provided by the county of Buckingham, where the County Council has provided a part-time organiser for such activities in recognition of their valuable educational role. Considerable expansion of this type of voluntary work could take place if a better system of organisation were established. There is certainly no shortage of work — especially outside nature reserves — and it is highly desirable that many more young people should take part and thus be encouraged to take an active interest in the countryside. An obvious first step is to involve other youth organisations (Scouts, Guides, Youth Clubs, etc.) who can supply parties for specific tasks without increasing the administrative load on the local Conservation Corps. Perhaps this could be achieved as part of a wider move by County Naturalists' Trusts and other Conservation bodies to interest these youth organisations in the understanding and care of their countryside.

In April 1970 a new charitable trust, The British Trust for Conservation Volunteers, was launched and the Conservation Corps gained independence from the Council for Nature. The Conservation Corps forms the field force of the new Trust, and numbers of volunteers are expected to grow rapidly as local Corps branches are set up in major centres of population. Branches will organize week-

end tasks in their own areas and will also join in the national programme of residential tasks. Independent conservation corps groups,
such as those organized among the members of a Naturalists' Trust,
will be invited to become affiliated to the British Trust for Conservation Volunteers.

VIII

FOOTPATHS AND NATURE CONSERVATION

P. W. RICHARDS, M.A., SC.D., F.L.S.

North Wales Naturalists' Trust

FOR THOSE WHO CARE for the British flora and fauna and for beautiful scenery, a cause for serious anxiety is population pressure, not only in its current figurative meaning, but in its most literal sense, the pressure of millions of human feet. This is a pressure which can be measured in pounds per square inch and in any area like the splendid National Nature Reserves of Wales, visited every year by crowds of people in search of recreation or instruction, it is steadily increasing. It represents one of the greatest threats to natural vegetation, and consequently to the associated animal life and to the appearance of the landscape.

If a lawn is walked over too often it becomes threadbare like a worn-out coat, but natural plant communities such as rough grazings and heather-covered moors suffer far more from treading because moorland grasses unlike the turf-forming grasses of lawns have not become adapted by long-continued selection to this kind of treatment. Some wild plants, mostly weeds, which normally live in close contact with man and his activities, flourish when constantly trodden on and some actually seem to prefer trodden to untrodden ground. One such plant is the slender rush *(Juncus tenuis)*, a species introduced to North Wales from America some eighty or more years ago. One of its favourite habitats is the gravelly edges of by-roads; sometimes it extends into grassy fields, but always keeping to paths and bare patches trampled by cattle. This is partly because its sticky mucilaginous seeds are easily distributed by hoofs, feet and wheels, but also because it is tough and extremely resistant to treading. Other examples are silverweed *(Potentilla anserina)* and the American mayweed *(Matricaria matricarioides)*, both plants common near farm buildings; they seem uninjured by treading and even to benefit from it.

These species are mentioned as exceptions; wild plants in general do not enjoy being trodden on. Treading bruises their leaves, crushes their stems and by compacting the soil, destroys its natural structure, so reducing the aeration of the roots. If population pressure, in the

41

literal sense, is heavy enough, the natural plant covering may be completely destroyed, leading in time to extensive areas of bare soil which are readily eroded by rain water when wet and by wind when dry. Even among ordinary wild plants sensitiveness to treading varies, and it is obvious that some species and some types of plant community are less tolerant than others. Little research has been done on this since Peace and Gilmour's experiments of twenty years ago (*New Phytol;* 48, 115-117, 1949) which showed how much more harmful trampling was to bluebells than picking the flowers or most other types of ill-treatment.

Sand dunes colonized by tufts of the marram grass such as those at Newborough Warren, Morfa Harlech, Towyn, Kenfig Burrows and elsewhere on the Welsh coast, are particularly sensitive to public pressure, because the habitat is in any case mobile and affected by constant wind erosion. The marram, though remarkably resistant to many forms of ill-treatment, cannot carry out its function of consolidating and fixing the dune sand if it has to contend with heavy human pressure as well as the natural hazards of its habitat. If one looks down on Morfa Harlech from the viewpoint to the south of the castle, the dunes appear in general green and fairly well covered with natural vegetation or planted trees, except in two areas, one to the north which has even now barely recovered from the bombing and other military activities of the last war, and the other where the dunes are crossed by the path from the village to the beach. Here it is the feet of thousands of visitors which have done the damage.

In Holland the coastal dunes are valued not only as a precious amenity but are vitally important to the country because of the natural store of fresh water contained in the sand which forms an important part of the country's limited water resources. Enormous pains are taken to protect the marram and other natural plant covering as far as possible. When sections of the dunes show signs of damage from public pressure, they are fenced off for a while to give them a chance to recover. In some places brushwood is laid on the surface of the sand to combat excessive erosion. On the fore dunes at Newborough Warren the Forestry Commission uses similar methods to protect the young conifer plantations.

Damage to dune vegetation in Wales is still localized, but could become serious if pressure increases still further. Dunes denuded of their natural vegetation become dangerous masses of shifting sand which can menace agricultural land and buildings lying far inland. Some years ago efforts were made to popularize 'sand skiing' on the Anglesey coast. Fortunately only a passing interest in this developed; had it proved a popular sport much marram would have been destroyed and the results for the dunes could have been disastrous.

Other habitats where the ground is naturally unstable and moving, however slowly, such as screes and mountain slopes subject to 'soil creep' and solifluction are, like sand dunes, especially vulnerable to the effects of human feet. This is because the equilibrium between vegetation and soil is precarious and the grasses, ferns, lichens and mosses which are the chief colonizers of such areas cannot cope with the additional mobility caused by the traffic. Anyone who climbs Snowdon by the Pig Track, the Miners' Path or Watkin Path can see for himself the disastrous effects of excessive treading on surfaces of this kind.

The plant covering of peaty moorlands and heaths on acid sandy soils, which largely consists of wiry plants such as the heath rush *(Juncus squarrosus)*, the common rush *(Juncus effusus)*, mat grass and the purple moor-grass, might be expected to stand a great deal of wear and tear and indeed it does, yet eventually even moorland grasses can stand no more. In the 1920's and 1930's a few square yards of *Nardus* remained on the sandy slopes of Hampstead Heath, actually within the County of London. The *Nardus* was exposed to an almost unimaginably heavy public pressure, but some time during the succeeding thirty years the erosion became so great that *Nardus* has almost vanished to be replaced by such urban grasses as Italian rye-grass *(Lolium multiflorum)* and annual poa *(Poa annua)*, probably sown there by the London Parks Department. A similar change has overtaken many commons in the neighbourhood of London and other large cities.

Peaty ground is naturally more easily damaged when it is wet and soft than when it is dry, and on Snowdon there are shocking examples of peat eroded by walkers' feet to unsightly quagmires: one of the worst is on the lower part of the Pig Track, in the hollow before it climbs towards the ridge of Crib Goch.

In the heavily populated British islands the national parks and nature reserves must inevitably be places where vast numbers of people go for recreation and study: for the most part they cannot be wilderness inhabited only by wild animals and where wild flowers 'waste their sweetness on the desert air'. At most we can try to preserve a few secluded areas for shy creatures such as the kite *(Milvus milvus)* whose very existence seems incompatible with any but the most sparse human populations. Whether naturalists welcome them or not, increasing numbers of people will walk over the heaths, dunes, mountains and moorlands of Britain, and if the wild plants and animals are to survive, means must be found of giving free access to such areas with as little damage as possible to the natural ecosystems.

It is not sufficiently realised that one of the most useful ways of promoting the conservation of nature and natural landscapes is to provide well-made, properly maintained footpaths. Where such paths already exist the majority of people follow them; they do not sprawl up a mountain like an invading army causing a vast amount of quite unnecessary erosion, as they now do on parts of Snowdon. Comparatively few wish to stray from recognized paths and in a large area such as Snowdonia it would be unnecessary as well as unpopular to enforce a 'keep to the footpath' policy. At present the steeper parts of the Miners' Track are full of boulders and loose pebbles; in wet weather they are running streams. A sensible person instinctively walks anywhere but on the path itself. The erosion from the feet of the walkers who walk not on but beside the path, or along some supposedly better route to right or left, causes the grass to wear away and so the damage quickly spreads.

If paths are to have any effect in canalizing the traffic in the way suggested they need to be carefully graded and not too steep or too roundabout; they must have a hard, free-draining surface, and be wide enough for several people to walk abreast. They need not have a tarmacadam surface or concrete kerbs which would be quite out of keeping with the environment and justify the complaints of those who say the mountains and wild places are being suburbanized. Paths are needed, but they need not spoil the scenery or damage plant life. This is admirably demonstrated in the Alps of France, Switzerland and Austria where a first-rate system of footpaths, far better than those in our own mountains, has existed for many years. These paths are built and maintained by the local authorities who have long realized their value, both as an amenity attracting tourists and as a means of reducing damage to hayfields and pastures. Many alpine paths are colour-coded by means of unobtrusive paint marks on boulders here and there, avoiding the need for many signposts.

As yet very little of this kind has been attempted in Britain other than the Countryside Commission's paths for long distance walkers. Most mountain paths in Wales are rapidly deteriorating because it is nobody's business to make or maintain them: the landowners and tenant farmers can hardly be expected to do so. Yet some progress has been made. Tribute must be paid to the excellent work of volunteer bodies such as the Council for Nature's Conservation Corps and Dr R. G. Gibbs's enthusiastic Conservation Group at Bangor, who have done much to fight erosion and repair paths in various parts of Snowdonia. This year, as a contribution to E.C.Y., the Ramblers' Association has launched a National Footpaths Week. This is admirable and deserves every success. Understandably the Ramblers wish to keep alive rights of way in danger of being lost, to clear paths in wooded and agricultural areas in danger of being overgrown, and to make new paths where there is little public access at present. They also want to demonstrate that 'the conservation of paths can be tackled by those who care for them'. These are the aims which most naturalists would support, though whether the task is wholly within the capacity of voluntary organizations is, as Dr. Gibbs points out, perhaps doubtful. Should not the construction and maintenance of paths be a high priority for the Countryside Commission, the Nature Conservancy and the local authorities?

Those who knew Wales forty years ago may think a little regretfully of the days when one could wander freely almost anywhere and had almost a free choice of sites to pitch a tent. Conditions have now changed so much that in many places this is no longer possible. Nobody welcomes even a small loss of freedom, but it has to be recognized that there have to be prepared camping sites and well marked footpaths. Only by accepting a few reasonable restraints will it be possible to preserve nature or anything 'natural' in such a highly populated island as Britain. If we do nothing a large part of the natural plant cover will disappear and with it most of the beauty of the landscape — literally worn away by millions of human feet.

IX

FORESTRY AND WILDLIFE IN WALES

F. C. BEST, O.B.E., B.A.

Forestry Commission (retired) and *North Wales Naturalists' Trust*

IN PLIOCENE TIMES coniferous woodland was widespread in Wales and the Norway spruce *(Picea abies)* and Scots pine *(Pinus sylvestris)* grew mixed with native hardwoods. In Britain probably all woodland was eliminated during the Ice Age and the Norway spruce never managed to return unaided by man but the Scots pine became re-established and ultimately retreated to the Highlands of Scotland. The remains of timber of mountain ash *(Sorbus aucuparia)*, birch and occasionally of oak can be found in the peat quite high up on the Welsh hills and it is believed that these species grew up to elevations of nearly 2000 ft. only a few thousand years ago.

The native woods of Wales of early historic times were mainly of pedunculate oak *(Quercus robur)* on the rich soils of the valley bottoms and sessile oak *(Quercus petraea)* on the thin and more acid soils of the hillsides. Alder occupied wet lowland areas and ash was often present on streamsides and where spring water raised the base status of the soil, and on outcrops of limestone or on basic igneous rock.

Birch seldom if ever forms a climax forest in Wales but occurs following felling and fire and is usually the first step in recolonization by oak; but in recent post-glacial times it may have occurred as open forest, pure or mixed with mountain ash and hawthorn *(Crataegus monogyna)* at the upper limit of tree growth. The very interesting woods on limestone mainly in South Wales contain ash and beech *(Fagus sylvatica)* and small-leaved lime *(Tilia cordata)*, once widespread but now very restricted in Britain, and several endemic species of white beam *(Sorbus)*. Wych elm *(Ulmus glabra)* is a sporadic tree in most types of native Welsh woodland.

Climatic change was largely responsible for the retreat of trees from the higher altitudes but the activities of man and his grazing animals have accelerated the loss of woodland which is still going on more rapidly than the casual observer might suppose. The use of wood for fuel and of oak for fencing has fallen off with rising labour costs and greater affluence but the increased sheep stocks have nullified any benefit derived from myxomatosis and the native woodland area is still contracting owing to the failure of natural regeneration in the presence of grazing animals.

The woods retreated to the lower ground where soil and climate were more favourable and where the trees were able to withstand grazing pressure. They also retreated to the rocky hillsides where stock grazing was light. Heavy grazing has changed the character of the vegetation and woody plants such as the heaths *(Erica cinerea, E. tetralix)*, heather, bilberry and gorse *(Ulex* species) have been greatly reduced in distribution and extent and replaced by grasses and bracken *(Pteridium aquilinum)*. These changes are continuing and are accelerated by burning and still further prevent the return of native woodland as both grass and bracken form unfavourable conditions for the natural regeneration of woodland. The large areas of mountain land now being planted are reversing this process but the distribution and character of the new woods is admittedly very different from that of the old ones.

The first step in afforestation is enclosure of the land to stop grazing by stock and rabbits. The immediate effect is the flowering and seeding of the grasses and other plants to the benefit of seed-eating birds. When the roots of heather, bilberry and gorse remain alive these plants reassert themselves. On dry, sandy and very infertile sites, where grass turf does not exclude all else, flowering plants immediately reappear. The sand dunes of Newborough became a botanist's paradise in the early days of planting; and the limestone screes of Eglwyseg and of the north Denbighshire coast blossomed with common rockrose *(Helianthemum chamaecistus)*, vipers bugloss *(Echium vulgare)* and other rarer flowers. On mountain grassland sometimes great clumps of hairbells *(Campanula rotundifolia)*, bog asphodel *(Narthecium ossifragum)* and mountain pansy *(Viola lutea)* appear in unexpected places.

It is often stated that the chalk downlands of the south of England lose their flowers and their butterflies when grazing by sheep and rabbits is stopped. This is no doubt so on the more fertile soils that used to be grazed by the heavier breeds of sheep but there are cases on the chalk downland where enclosure for afforestation has resulted in profuse development of flowering plants and their attendant butterflies. The Welsh sheep grazes everything hard down and the tough mountain grasses seem best able to withstand this treatment. So the exclusion of sheep usually results in an increase in flowering plants in Welsh hill land.

Following enclosure of acid moorlands the preparatory work of ploughing, draining and fertilizing takes place and this has a varied effect on the vegetation; bracken receives a check, grasses such as

47

wavy hair grass *(Deschampsia flexuosa)* flower, and heather if present develops and flowers along the furrow edges. Gorse seed lying in the soil quickly germinates and may become dominant. Thyme *(Thymus serpyllum* agg.), trefoil *(Lotus corniculatus)* and mountain pansy may quickly colonise the upturned furrow. This is a temporary phase that persists only until the conifers grow enough to suppress the vegetation, and soon afterwards thinning of the trees starts.

After several thinnings the canopy opens up, more light reaches the ground and vegetation returns. But its character is different from that of the original ground: bracken is generally replaced by male fern *(Dryopteris filix-mas, D. borreri),* and brambles and grasses may return but no tight turf develops. Occasionally shrubs such as elder *(Sambucus nigra)* and holly *(Ilex aquifolium)* may appear particularly when seed-eating birds use the plantation for roosting. The older the tree crop the more vegetation returns, provided thinnings are regularly carried out.

After clear felling, some of the original species return and foxgloves *(Digitalis purpurea)* and willow herb *(Epilobium* species, most commonly *E. angustifolium)* appear and remain for a few years, the latter often high up on moorland areas. Birch and sallow *(Salix* species), also with wind-borne seed, may appear and sometimes seedlings of the felled conifers. These developments make far-reaching changes in the plant and animal life of a forest.

The conifers planted are mostly of the some genera as those of pre-glacial Britain but the species are different. It is surprising that trees native to Pacific coastal areas of North America or to parts of Japan thrive better in Wales than the trees of Europe even though some of them inhabited Britain before the Ice Age. The Scots pine, the only native coniferous timber tree to return to Britain after the Ice Age, retreated to the north of Scotland during the post-glacial period, where it evolved a local race more suited to our climate than the races of Continental Europe or of Scandinavia, but even the native Scottish race thrives best in the drier eastern part of the country. Had the Norway spruce survived the Ice Age in Britain it might well have evolved a race more suited to stand up to the sea winds of our west coast.

In Wales we have none of the plants of northern Britain associated with conifer forests such as chickweed wintergreen *(Trientalis europaea),* Linnaea *(Linnaea borealis),* one-flowered wintergreen *(Moneses uniflora),* creeping lady's tresses *(Goodyera repens)* but broad-leaved helleborine *(Epipactis helleborine),* a rather rare plant in Wales, sometimes favours fir plantations in the pole stage.

It follows that evergreen forests of shade-bearing species in full production cannot support a prolific ground vegetation because the light is largely utilized by the trees. Deciduous forest permits a ground vegetation to grow and flower in early spring before the full tree leaf crop suppresses it. Larch (*Larix* species) is not only deciduous but a light demanding tree giving a low yield of timber because it needs much space and allows more light through the canopy and permits more vegetation to grow under it.

Condry (*Quarterly Journal of Forestry*, Vol. LIV No. 4, October 1960) has shown how the bird population changes as a plantation develops on bare mountain land. First food and cover develop by the growth of plants protected from grazing and birds such as skylarks, meadow pipits, tree pipits, grasshopper warblers and black grouse and, where heather had previously been overgrazed, red grouse increase. The short-eared owl may come in following increase of voles. As the trees grow and the cover becomes denser pipits, larks and red grouse go out but yellowhammers, linnets, whitethroats, willow warblers, robins, wrens and hedge sparrows increase. With further growth all the ground-nesting birds leave and bullfinches, redpolls, blackbirds, songthrushes and garden warblers continue.

Up to this stage there has been an increase in species and total numbers, but from now on species and numbers decline and birds such as crows, jays, magpies, woodpigeons and the more truly 'conifer birds' such as goldcrests and coaltits occupy the woods. As the trees develop in size and as thinning opens up the crop the birds of prey find nesting sites and buzzards, kestrels, sparrowhawks, tawny owls and long-eared owls may take up residence; and sometimes siskins breed in the tree tops. Crossbills come in some years and feed on the cones but breeding has yet to be proved. Even ravens and herons are known to breed in conifer plantations.

The colonisation of the forest by mammals follows a similar pattern to that of birds. Small rodents in mountain grassland often increase following afforestation and stoats, weasels and polecats benefit for a while. The pine marten, in spite of its name, is not primarily a beast of conifer forests, preferring rocky ground with some trees. Although reported from time to time in Forestry Commission forests it has not yet shown any real tendency to colonize conifer forests in Wales. Fox, badger and otter seem to be little affected by afforestation. Foxes have certainly increased during the last half century but factors other than afforestation may have been responsible. The badger seems to have increased in Wales a century or so ago and is now holding its own, but the status of the otter all over Britain is in some doubt.

Deer present a problem to forestry owing to the great damage they can do, but the Forestry Commission has devoted much study to the problem of reducing damage. By a proper system of culling and maintaining numbers at a satisfactory level and the ages and sexes in correct proportion it is found that a population can be maintained without serious damage and the loss can be offset against revenue obtained from deer shooting. Over Britain as a whole half a dozen species of deer have spread during the last twenty years but so far only a few semi-wild fallow deer live in the woods in certain parts of Wales, but other species may come.

Of insects a number of new species of beetles, moths and sawflies have come into the forests from the countries of origin of the conifers but all are small and uninteresting to the general naturalist. There are no British butterflies dependent on conifers and there are only two native hardwood timber trees that provide the foodplant for the caterpillars of any British butterflies. The purple hairstreak *(Thecla quercus)* feeds on oak and is a forest dweller; but the large tortoiseshell *(Nymphalis polychloros)* and the white-letter hairstreak *(Strymonidia w-album)* both feed on wych elm often on the margins of woods or ride-sides or in hedgerows. Other woodland species feed on nettles, violet, grasses, crucifers, sloe, gorse, primrose and buckthorn and the presence of these plants and of wide rides is essential for their existence. Bramble flowers are much favoured by woodland butterflies and so are thistles and devils-bit scabious *(Succisa pratensis)*; but conifer forests, even when these plants are available, are not generally favoured by woodland butterflies which prefer the native oak woods.

The mountain grasslands which provide the major area for afforestation work in Wales are relatively sparsely populated by birds and the forest which replaces it supports a greater number of species and individuals especially when the forest reaches 'normality', that is when there is an even distribution of age classes and therefore a complete range of habitat and that rather useful 'verge effect' where one type passes into the next.

Normality in a forest cannot be achieved until planting has continued for full rotation age, say fifty to sixty years. But many small areas of advanced growth are now being felled in Forestry Commission forests to help new timber consuming industries to become established and these fellings together with inevitable windfalls are rapidly breaking up the uniformity of the older Forestry Commission forests. It is to be hoped, however, that this process will not go too far and that ultimately fellings will not take place before maturity.

The replacement of deciduous hardwood forests with conifers results in a reduction in wild life of all kinds. Of all trees the oak supports more wild life than any other and mixed woodland with a high proportion of oak widely spaced with plenty of understorey of shrubs and numerous wide rides is the most prolific.

What is the future of Welsh woodlands as wildlife sanctuaries? Much is said about 'multiple land use' but it must be recognised that

PLATE 3. *Above*, buzzard and young in Breconshire, probably the commonest bird-of-prey in the county. On sunny winter days small parties can often be seen soaring effortlessly overhead. *Right*, male pied flycatcher at the nest-hole. A frequent breeding bird in the upland woods of Breconshire and elsewhere in Wales.

if the object of managing a woodland or forest is the economic production of timber then management must be directed to that end and it would be wrong to spend money uneconomically to further other interests. However, the management of commercial forests can be modified so that wildlife conservation is catered for to some extent provided it is recognised that this must be paid for either in the form of increased costs or lower production of timber or both.

Whether engaged in state or private forestry a technically trained forester is expected to have some knowledge of wildlife conservation. That this is taken seriously by professional foresters is shown by the fact that the Society of Foresters of Great Britain held a three day discussion meeting in 1967 on 'Wild Life in the Forest' attended by over sixty members and nineteen papers were read covering a wide range of subjects. Scotland's special problem of 'Red Deer and Forestry' formed the subject of a one day symposium organised by the Royal Scottish Forestry Society the same year.

In a country as highly populated as Britain it is necessary to obtain as high a yield of timber as possible from a minimum area and any reduction in timber production from a given area requires an extension of forest area to produce the same volume of timber. The extent to which economic timber production and wildlife conservation can be combined is therefore primarily a matter of the objects of management and secondarily it depends on the skill of management.

As has been shown above, the establishment of a commercial coniferous forest on an area of grass moorland adds to the wildlife of the area as a whole by creating a different and more varied habitat. Other forest operations can contribute something also: road construction requires fairly wide rides and the rather hard scars made by new roads along the contours of steep hillsides gradually heal and provide sites for common, but none the less beautiful, wild flowers such as foxgloves, thyme, trefoil, hairbells, bedstraw, scabious and a fringe habitat for birds such as black grouse, where seeding plants and grasses and pine buds can be found and where grit and dusting is available. Quarries for road construction are bare and ugly at first but old quarries always provide a habitat for plants of some sort. Small ponds are sometimes made to provide water for fire-fighting and these can be attractive places for wildfowl and other birds as well as for plant and insect life.

A very useful development in commercial forestry is the increasing value placed on game and although large coniferous forests are not usually very productive of game, methods can be adopted for improving them such as retaining open ground, growing game crops, retaining areas of scrub and making duck pools. Any such areas that are beneficial for game are beneficial for other forms of wildlife.

51

Gamekeepers in the past have been accused of destroying all species of predators but the Game Research Association and the Eley Game Service have now combined to form the Game Conservancy which, working in close association with the Nature Conservancy, is training gamekeepers with a more enlightened outlook. It is now appreciated that while vigorous control of some of the commoner predators is necessary the rarer ones can be preserved without much sacrifice of game. Furthermore, birds other than game benefit by the control of crows and foxes and the rarer predators can benefit by the preservation of prey species. Harriers have nested in Wales in recent years in forest areas where foxes and crows have been controlled. This is due in part to the suitable cover provided by plantations in the very young stages but probably more to the increase in the bird population on which they prey.

Forestry in the past has been carried out mainly on land unsuited to or not particularly required for other purposes but it is hoped that more enlightened land planning will prevail in the future. Commercial forestry should be confined to land where good growth can be obtained and where costs of establishment and of timber production are satisfactory. In Wales that is mainly on the mountain grasslands and bracken covered slopes. Forestry involves a high capital investment compared with mountain grazing, so a high yield is necessary in order to obtain even a modest return on capital.

Heather moorland has a high potential value for sport and when properly managed it can produce both grouse and sheep and afford a degree of public recreation. It is seldom high grade forest land and it is always a severe fire risk. It provides a wildlife habitat rather different from grass moorlands.

Much of the limited area of native, semi-native and scrub woodland remaining in Wales is by reason of its size, shape, topography or condition not very suitable for commercial forestry. So it is hoped that some of these will be managed primarily for conservation of wild life by the Nature Conservancy or the Naturalists' Trusts, and that others will be managed by their owners for amenity, game preservation and shelter as well as for timber production and conservation of wildlife.

It is hoped that an enlightened government will provide financial assistance and help to owners or occupiers to plant and maintain small spinneys for amenity and conservation purposes to replace the fast disappearing hedgerows and to grow high grade hardwood timber.

Commercial forestry can play an increased part in conservation so long as it is recognised that any departure from maximum production of timber has to be paid for, even though the price may not be large.

Leaving unplanted small areas of marsh or bog, stream and lakesides, retaining small areas of hardwood trees, planting small areas of hardwoods, making small areas of still water with a surround of marshland and maintaining some wider than normal rides are all small things that can materially increase the wildlife of a forest without great cost.

The Forestry Commission is well qualified to do these things but how far they can and should go is a matter of government policy. Other woodland owners whether corporate bodies, city financiers, traditional landowners, farm occupiers or forestry enthusiasts may have an equal or greater need to make their woods pay. To a forester there is beauty in well-grown timber but as every forester should and usually does appreciate nature, he sees beauty in trees apart from their timber and also in wildlife — things which give us all satisfaction and peace of mind in a world of stress and hurry.

X

NATURE CONSERVATION IN BRECONSHIRE

M. PORTER, B.SC.

Brecknock County Naturalists' Trust

BRECONSHIRE HAS AN AREA of roughly 726 square miles, just over half of which (381 square miles) lies within the Brecon Beacons National Park designated in 1957. 'Brecnocshire is very montanius, and in sum place very wooddy; nevertheless in the valles fruteful of corn and especially of pastures' wrote Leland about 1540. Corn is no longer so much in evidence, but the mountains still impress visitors.

Over half the county lies at above 1000 feet. Pen-y-fan, almost 3000 ft. (Plate 1) the highest Old Red sandstone summit in the British Isles, with its northern escarpments sharply incised by glacial action, stands sentinel over the Usk valley. The long flank of the Black Mountains which form the boundary with Herefordshire in the east is also Old Red sandstone. The centre of the county is occupied by the more rounded mass of Mynydd Eppynt dissected by many tumbling dipper-haunted streams, Cilieni, Bran, Yscir and Honddu, which race south-wards to join the Usk. Mynydd Eppynt is occupied by the Army which has almost 28 000 acres as an artillery range. On its northern slopes Silurian mudstones and shales outcrop and these are found over much of the north of the county, except where a diagonal band of Ordovician rock runs northeastwards from Llanwrtyd Wells towards the Wye just south of Rhayader. There is dramatic mountain scenery in these parts, notably in the Irfon valley north of Abergwesyn, where in autumn the rich golden tints of the hanging oakwoods blend with the rufous bracken on the mountainsides.

The southern boundary of Breconshire is bordered by barren hills like Mynydd Llangynidr and Mynydd Llangattock, where a belt of Carboniferous limestone outcrops around the northern rim of the South Wales Coalfield. The south is rich in interesting limestone escarpments, swallow holes and underground caverns, and renowned for its spectacular waterfalls.

The landscape owes much of its character to the Ice Age. Its influence is apparent in the steep, northern scarps of the Beacons, with cirques at their bases gouged out by glaciers, now occupied by lakes like Llyn Cwm-llwch and Llyn y Fan Fawr. Gradually, as the ice retreated, an arctic tundra type of vegetation developed, relicts of which still survive on the northern facing precipices at Craig Cwm-sere and Craig Cerrig-gleisiad. Later, forests developed in the valleys and on the mountain sides and maintained their sway until man began, about 4500 years ago, slowly but surely to clear the forests for his crops and animals. The long cairns, burial places of these first Neolithic farmers in Breconshire, may be seen in the foothills of the Black Mountains at Ty-isaf near Talgarth and Ffostyll near Llanelieu. The forest clearance gained momentum, at first for agriculture and later, in the seventeenth and eighteenth centuries, for the forges and ironworks of the Industrial Revolution. Breconshire oak also had a high reputation for its quality in shipbuilding. In recent years tree felling has accelerated and now only relicts of the native deciduous woods can be found on the very steep slopes and in dingles, such as Coed Dyrysiog in the Nant Bran and the wooded Cwm Pwll-y-wrach.

Breconshire is still predominantly an agricultural county with a strong emphasis on sheep. The high altitude and heavy rainfall over much of the county conspire to make corn crops uncertain and the acreage has fallen from 36 000 acres in 1872 to 11 000 in 1967. Grazing has been for centuries the chief biotic factor influencing the vegetation. Agricultural returns for 1966 show 144 000 acres of grassland and nearly 244 000 acres of rough grazing. Roughly three quarters of the county is therefore clothed with moorland and grassland, the balance between these being determined by grazing and, in recent years, changes in farming practice. Reduction in the number of cattle and increasing labour costs have hastened the spread of bracken over considerable areas of hillside grassland. A smaller number of wethers on the hills early in the spring has tended to favour the spread of coarse grasses like matgrass to the detriment of the better pasture grasses like sheep's fescue and common bent.

Grassland dominated by these last two species, but with sweet vernal grass (*Anthoxanthum odoratum*) and such small herbs as tormentil (*Potentilla erecta*) and heath bedstraw (*Galium saxatile*) usually in attendance, occupies much of the zone between the enclosed fields and the moorland above. On most upland farms there are marshy or boggy patches where springs seep from the hillside. In the limestone and sandstone regions a fairly base-rich peat has sometimes developed and in summer such patches are gay with the handsome purple heads of meadow thistle (*Cirsium dissectum*), mixed populations of spotted orchid (*Dactylorhiza* species) and sometimes a few clumps of the yellow globeflower (*Trollius europaeus*). This type of plant community is decreasing. Dwindling populations can sometimes be found in areas which have been ploughed and drained and where rank upon rank of small conifers now stand. The Woolhope Naturalists' Field Club, reporting an excursion in 1866, describes walking down from Mynydd Troed to Llangorse lake through 'Several meadows refulgent with Globeflowers'. One would have to travel a long way to see a sight like that nowadays! The Brecknock Naturalists' Trust is seeking to conserve an interesting wetland on Cefn Bola Maen where red rattle *(Pedicularis palustris)*, lesser skullcap *(Scutellaria minor)* and creeping willow *(Salix repens)* are flourishing at present.

Sheep may sometimes be the naturalists' allies. The closely-grazed limestone pastures, like that below Daren Disgwylfa, allow many interesting small herbs like autumn gentian *(Gentianella amarella)*, blue fleabane *(Erigeron acris)*, carline and stemless thistles *(Carlina vulgaris* and *Cirsium acaule)* to thrive and are the favourite haunts of the grayling *(Eumenis semele)* and common blue *(Polyommatus icarus)* butterflies.

Much of the grassland zone was formerly wooded; mainly sessile oak or birch in the north and west, ash on the limestone and alder in the damp patches. Most small deciduous woods that remain are accessible to sheep and frequently used for sheltering them during hard winter weather, as at Coed-y-croftau in the Beacons. Consequently, the woods tend to have an impoverished ground flora and show little sign of natural regeneration.

The effects of agriculture on the wildlife in the county are not nearly as far reaching as in many parts of the British Isles, particularly where there is intensive arable farming. Few hedgerows, such valuable sanctuaries for many animals and plants, have been removed and, incidentally, it is good to note the County Council replanting hedge-rows after road widening schemes, contrary to the practice in at least one neighbouring county! Hill farming subsidies have led to the ploughing up and reseeding of most old pastures; others have been improved by dressings of artificial fertilisers; but there are still a few fascinating examples of old, floristically rich pastures in out of the way places around the county. The Naturalists' Trust is at present negotiating to conserve one wonderful example in the north of Breconshire where greater butterfly orchid *(Platanthera chlorantha)*, wood horsetail *(Equisetum sylvaticum)*, yellow rattle *(Rhinanthus* species) and bitter vetch *(Vicia orobus)* all flourish. The bitter vetch, now known from only a handful of localities, was probably the first rare plant to be recorded for Breconshire, being noted by William Camden in his 'Britannia'.

Another fortunate consequence of the small area of arable is that the use of pesticides has been fairly limited. As a result, seed-eating birds, like chaffinches, and their predators have not been killed in such huge numbers as in parts of eastern England between 1956 and

1963. The voluntary ban on the use of the persistent organo-chlorine dieldrin in sheep dips probably came just in time for the buzzard. In (Plate 3). In the Brecknock Naturalists' Trust Newsletter in October 1964 Dr C. M. Fenn estimated that the buzzard population in north Breconshire had been reduced by a third over the previous seven years and that many of the survivors were sterile. Since then it has been conclusively shown that infertility and abnormal behaviour, such as egg-breaking, may result in birds-of-prey, through the build up in their food chains of persistent organo-chlorine pesticides. In the late 1950's and early this decade the peregrine falcon disappeared from most, if not all, of its former haunts in the county, as at Abergwesyn where it bred up to 1960. It had probably never been common, though Ingram and Salmon record in ' Birds of Brecknock' that an average of five eyries were regularly tenanted up to about 1956. Peregrines and sparrowhawks have been decimated by these persistent pesticides which, in the case of the peregrines, were presumably accumulated mainly during the winter migration by eating birds such as pigeons which had fed on corn dressed with these poisons. The long term effects of persistent pesticides on a host of other animals, including man himself, are still not fully known. The Trust has recently been pressing for a ban on D.D.T., another organo-chlorine pesticide, and closer control over the labelling and sale of other poisonous chemicals. Many other countries, including recently Canada, have taken the decision to ban D.D.T. and it is clearly time that a re-assessment was made on a world-wide basis.

The sovereignty of sheep has been challenged in recent years over a large part of its former territory by conifers, which are rapidly replacing them and the remaining deciduous woods. In 1924, five years after its establishment, when the Forestry Commission carried out a country-wide census of woodlands, over 85% of the 28 000 acres of woodland recorded for Breconshire were composed of native broad-leaved trees. In 1962 Hyde and Guile estimated in 'Plant life in Brecknock' that broad-leaved trees then comprised about 50% of the total woodland area. In 1969 there are approaching 50 000 acres of conifers while the acreage of broad-leaved trees has rapidly dwindled. Since the 1947-49 Forestry Commission census which recorded 17 000 acres of deciduous woodland, many thousands of acres of these have been felled and replaced by conifers as, for example, the ash woods in the limestone valleys of Cwm Claisfer and Dyffryn Crawnon — both within the Brecon Beacons National Park, and many of the oak hangers in the north of the county. A comparison of the one inch Ordnance Survey maps of 1952 and 1967 will underline this change. The remaining deciduous woods are small and now probably account for less than 20% of the total woodland area.

Compared with moorland which the conifers frequently replace there is, as Frank Best has indicated, an increase in birdlife in the plantations. Such birds as goldcrests and redpolls are spreading as a result of the increase in coniferous forests. However, these forests will almost certainly never at any stage support such diverse populations of plants and animals as our native deciduous woods, which often contain several species of trees of different ages, and a varied ground flora to provide food for many types of insects, which in turn support a considerable bird population. As the conifers spread over thousands of acres of old woods and moorland, as in the Abergwesyn region, not only are woodland birds like green woodpeckers and nuthatches losing their habitat but many of the characteristic moorland birds like golden plovers, buzzards and meadow pipits, are finding their feeding territories severely reduced and their populations are bound to decline. Such handsome insects as the emperor moth, whose caterpillars seemed more frequent than usual this year on the heather in the north of the county, will also be adversely affected. The conifers are so closely planted that lack of light, combined often with drainage operations and the accumulation of an acidic humus from the carpet of conifer needles, completely eliminates all the typical woodland herbs. Thus wood anemones (*Anemone nemorosa*), sanicle (*Sanicula euopaea*), herb Paris (*Paris quadrifolia*), goldilocks (*Ranunculus auricomus*) and even bluebells (*Endymion nonscriptus*) are getting fewer every year. Two flowers, the pale wood violet (*Viola reichenbachiana*) and a sedge (*Carex lepidocarpa*) may even be exterminated in Breconshire as a direct result of recent re-afforestation in Dyffryn Crawnon and Cwm Claisfer.

Of course, forestry is a large and important national industry and the Forestry Commission has done a great deal in recent years to foster the wildlife and improve the amenity value of its forests in many parts. But, if we accept the definition of a National Park used by the Hobhouse Report which led to the establishment of the National Parks under the 1949 Act, there must surely be a strong case for the conservation of all the more interesting remaining deciduous woods. As the White Paper on Nature Conservation published in 1947 observes: ' One of the chief differences between a National Park area and one of ordinary countryside is the greater interest in nature shown by the visiting public . . . the areas selected as National Parks contain large stretches of country as well as many smaller sites of high scientific value. That these valuable areas should be carefully conserved is inherent in the conception of a National Park '. Recognising the potential conflict between conservation and forestry, in the competition for marginal land and in the effects of conifers on existing wild life, the Hobhouse report went so far as to state: ' Trees and woodlands and the wealth of woodland fauna and flora will contribute so much to the beauty and interest of the Parks that their preservation and maintenance must be a vital factor in National Park planning' and, in a direct reference to the Brecon Beacons National Park: 'Agreement between the National Parks Commission, the Forestry Commission and private owners should set a limit to the clear felling of existing woodland and to the blanketing of moors and hillsides with conifer plantations in single age blocks'.

The report of the Wildlife Commission in 1947 recommended that a survey should be made of National Parks and all areas of scientific interest scheduled. This takes a long time and has still not been completed, largely because of the limited funds and shortage of staff available to the Nature Conservancy and the dearth of competent field workers to assist in local surveys. The results of the woodlands survey are now being assessed and other habitats are being investigated. The information is urgently needed and would be an invaluable aid to the Local Planning Authority and its Forestry Consultative Panel which considers specific afforestation proposals within the National Park. It is also vital knowledge for the Local Planning Authority in order to fulfil the charge laid upon them in the Countryside Act — 'The conservation and enhancement of the natural beauty and amenity of the countryside'. Too limited a concept of 'the natural beauty of the countryside' is often taken and the directive, given later in the Act that it should 'be construed as including references to the preservation of its flora, fauna and geological and physiographical features' has, all too often, been overlooked. Tree preservation orders can be made to protect special trees or woods of high amenity value and it is incumbent upon those who are interested in their environment to apply for them.

Much of the unenviable task of a National Park Authority involves controlling the siting and standard of necessary development schemes, so that new buildings and other constructions will not damage the character of the countryside. The proposed expansion scheme for Brecon, which is intended to lead to the doubling of the population during the next twenty years, presents a challenge to good planning of the environment. Some enterprising facilities for the enjoyment of the Park have already been provided. The Mountain Centre on Mynydd Illtyd, completed in 1966 with the aid of a Carnegie Trust grant, affords visitors the luxury of enjoying the splendour of the mountain scenery in comfort, and at the same time performs an excellent service, through the media of films, discussions and displays, in educating the visitors, 148 000 last year, to appreciate and conserve the countryside. In 1965 a warden was appointed to look after the Breconshire section of the National Park. He leads a very busy life supervising tree planting schemes, bridle path clearance, removal of litter and generally helping, with the aid of his band of seventy voluntary wardens, to safeguard the National Park.

The need for a greater knowledge of the ecology of our county has been emphasized as a necessary pre-requisite for any comprehensive plan for conservation. In common with many of the more remote rural counties, Breconshire has lagged behind in mapping its wildlife resources. In 'The Botanists' Guide through England and Wales' published in 1805, which noted the rarer plants on a county basis, only twenty plants were recorded for Breconshire as opposed to 388 for Sussex and 364 for Suffolk. After intense botanical exploration during the nineteenth century, in 1873 the Recorder of the Botanical Record Club reported that 'entirely new comital records . . . cannot now be numerous and must become rarer every year'. But it was not until the following year that Augustine Ley, a Herefordshire parson and redoubtable botanist, sent in the first systematic list of 100 common Breconshire plants, accompanied by voucher specimens. Since those early days much research and field work has been done in the county by such expert botanists as H. A. Hyde, A. E. Wade and D. P. M. Guile. 'Breconshire Birds' now published annually by the Naturalists' Trust, testifies to the volume of information about bird distribution which has been accumulated by many keen amateur ornithologists scattered around the county. In 1968 four new species were recorded for the county — grey plover, little gull, sanderling and Lapland bunting. Neither have the insects been entirely neglected: the Breconshire dragonflies have been studied extensively by David Kyle and the butterflies by J. P. Sankey-Barker.

Inevitably there is still much to be discovered about even the better known groups. In the first two years of our scheme to map the distribution of flowering plants and fern allies in the county, on a 5 × 5 kilometre square basis, seventeen new county records have been discovered, including such fascinating species as northern fen orchid (*Dactylorhiza purpurella*), orange foxtail (*Alopecurus aequalis*), sawsedge (*Cladium mariscus*) and pennyroyal (*Mentha pulegium*). No county flora has been published for Breconshire and we hope the information now being accumulated will ultimately be presented in this form.

Since the formation of a Conservation Committee in 1968 the Naturalists' Trust has made preliminary botanical surveys of well over a hundred habitats, and these have certainly emphasised the urgent need for conservation. Individual species sometimes pose intriguing problems. Why has the spreading bellflower (*Campanula patula*), described in 1800 as frequent around Crickhowell and noted in several other parts of the county, declined so considerably both here and in Herefordshire? There would appear to still be plenty of suitable lanes and rough banks.

During the past two years or so the status of the otter has caused much concern. Extensive enquiries among water bailiffs, fishermen and naturalists indicated a considerable decline in numbers of otters along the Usk since about 1960. Countrywide reports of falling otter populations led to an investigation by the Mammal Society being started in 1967. Their interim report published in February 1969 confirmed the decline here and in many other parts of the British Isles. In 1968, following an unsuccessful appeal to the Otter Hunt to stop hunting, until the results of the investigation were published and assessed, the Naturalists' Trust wrote to riparian owners on the Breconshire Usk and its tributaries seeking their co-operation in prohibiting otter hunting through their waters. No one would assert that otter hunting is solely responsible for the otters' decline. Their population, like that of the peregrine, seems to have been self-regulating and reasonably stable up to about 1960. The causes for its subsequent slump are at present unknown, but river pollution, increasing clearance and disturbance along river banks, shooting, trapping and hunting may all have played some part — though strangely enough few traces of persistent pesticides have been discovered in the few dead otters so far analysed. Hunting was one contributary factor which it was considered possible and desirable to limit. The response to the appeal was most favourable and 64% of the riparian owners supported it. It is hoped that this action may at least afford this attractive mammal some protection within a limited area until more extensive measures can be taken for its more general conservation.

The badger is likewise suffering from destruction of habitat and misguided persecution in many parts of the British Isles, including Breconshire. On at least six occasions last summer setts which had been dug out were found and by one was the tell-tale clue of a small dog's collar. Attempts must be made to prevent the unwarranted destruction of these useful animals by statutory measures and, in the long term, by the education of the people concerned to appreciate their countryside and its wild life.

But although many individual species need protection, it is the conservation of the most characteristic habitats that must be the primary aim. The Nature Conservancy has made an invaluable start by establishing four National Nature Reserves within the county, which include a fine series of cliff sites on a range of rock formations. They are all exciting places but, two of them hold a special appeal. Craig Cerrig-gleisiad, a magnificent, frowning, Old Red sandstone precipice, part of the northern escarpment of the Beacons, was the first to be declared in 1957-58. Its crumbling ledges are the home of

Arctic-alpine flowers such as purple saxifrage, roseroot (*Sedum rosea*) and cowberry (*Vaccinium vitis-idaea*) which flourish where even the sure-footed sheep cannot graze. The crags often echo to the harsh croaks of ravens, chattering calls of kestrels and, in summer, the scolding alarm notes of ring ouzels. Craig-y-cilau, declared a N.N.R. in 1959, is a Carboniferous limestone escarpment rising to 1500 feet, overlooking Crickhowell. J. E. Lousley in 'Wild flowers of Chalk and Limestone' describes it as the best place he knows for plants on inland limestone. It was here in 1893 that Augustine Ley discovered the lesser whitebeam (*Sorbus minima*) which has been found nowhere else in the world except on a neighbouring limestone crag. Few plants are so famous that they have caused questions in Parliament. In 1947 Ald. Tudor Watkins, M.P. for Brecon and Radnor, warned of the danger to this unique shrub from Mortar practice. Negotiations then led to the War Office declaring the cliff out of bounds to the Army. In the narrow crevices on the almost vertical cliffs grow an extraordinary array of rare shrubs and trees including both the small- and large-leaved limes, beech, yew (*Taxus baccata*) and four other sorts of whitebeams. At least seventeen species of ferns grow in this reserve and two alpine members, the brittle bladder fern (*Cystopteris fragilis*) and Dovedale moss (*Saxifraga hypnoides*), are frequent. Redstarts, in particular, find the crags an attractive breeding place; willow warblers are especially abundant on the shrubby screes below and a colony of black-headed gulls breeds on the little moorland pool above the cliff.

Cwm Clydach which contains the only significant relict of native, or semi-native, beech wood in South Wales, and Nant Irfon, with rugged moorland and fragments of oak-hangers, are the other two N.N.R.'s in Breconshire. A resident warden was appointed by the Nature Conservancy in 1968 to look after these fine reserves.

Twenty-three Sites of Special Scientific Interest (S.S.S.I.) have been notified in the county, two of which, the Towy Valley and the Neath and Mellte Valleys, cover a considerable area and wide range of habitats. Five are cave sites, of which there are some outstanding examples on the limestone, such as Ogof Ffynnon Ddu with a fine cave flora and fauna, and Ogof-y-ci famous for its blanched trout. Five are primarily of geological interest, while eight of the remainder contain fragments of deciduous woods.

There is intense pressure upon the remaining deciduous woods. Unfortunately, an S.S.S.I. designation does not yet confer a sufficient degree of protection. Although changes in land use such as building and quarrying may be prevented, there is no effective protection against re-afforestation which is their greatest threat. The 1968 Countryside Act appears to strengthen the hand of the Nature Conservancy in this matter. As the report of the Hobhouse Committee notes 'The native oak woods carpetted with mosses and ferns are a feature of the Brecon landscape the loss of which would be irreparable'. Prompt action is needed if they are to be saved and with them such beautiful butterflies as the purple hairstreak which seems to be mainly confined to the oak woods in the south east of the county.

The Naturalists' Trust has fortunately been able to make an informal nature reserve agreement for Craig-y-rhiwarth, described by some authorities as the finest ash-wood in South Wales. Fine communities of calcicole (lime-preferring) species, which include lily-of-the-valley (*Convallaria majalis*) and nodding melick (*Melica nutans*) carpet limestone ledges that are overhung by purging buckthorn (*Rhamnus catharticus*), spindle (*Euonymus europaeus*), yew and whitebeams on an escarpment commanding a beautiful view of the Tawe valley. The management policy will need to improve the regeneration of ash in this wood. An agreement is also being sought with the Forestry Commission to conserve another relict of ash-wood in Dyffryn Crawnon. This lies below an old tramway which runs around the head of the valley at about 1500 feet and gives walkers magnificent views of the deeply incised valley running eastwards, with the Black Mountains in the background. The view to the west is not improved by quarry waste heaps on the mountain which are spreading over the headwaters of the Crawnon stream and colouring its water a murky grey as they cascade over the escarpment. In spate this grey water can still be seen where the Crawnon meets the Usk five miles below. It is to be hoped that the quarry company will landscape and replant its tips when quarrying has moved on.

Negotiations are proceeding for the conservation of forty-two acres of a mountain wood in Nant Sere in the heart of the Brecon Beacons. The watershed and upper valley of the Sere are of outstanding biological interest. From below the northern precipice of Pen-y-fan, where several Arctic-alpine flowers like least willow and purple saxifrage reach their southernmost limit in the British Isles, the stream cascades rapidly over a series of waterfalls where at least one dipper's nest lies concealed by tussocks of Dovedale moss and water avens (*Geum rivale*). Woods of ash, alder and birch clothe both banks lower down and lime-rich flushes lead to some interesting plant communities. Over two hundred species of flowering plants and ferns have been recorded from the valley. Many fungi flourish in the damp conditions and an autumn visit to the wood can be a spectacular occasion. The beautiful but poisonous, scarlet and white-flecked fly agaric (*Amanita muscaria*) and many colourful species of *Russula* are frequent. Last summer the little orange clubs of the Topaz fungus (*Mitrula paludosa*) were unusually abundant on decaying alder leaves. Pied flycatchers (Plate 3), redstarts, tree pipits, nuthatches and other species of birds breed in the wood, supporting their families on a plentiful supply of insects. Researches by the Zoology Department of Cardiff University College have led to the discovery of two rare Arctic-alpine insects in this valley and the neighbouring Nant Cwm-llwch.

The National Trust has performed a magnificent service in preserving the entire central region of the Brecon Beacons, in all about 9000 acres, for the enjoyment of the public. In 1969 another 1000 acres were purchased with the aid of a grant, amounting to half the cost, from the Countryside Commission. Does this welcome and speedy action on the part of the Countryside Commission give hope of a more dynamic approach to preserve the dwindling countryside in the face of so many pressures? The Countryside Act should certainly help greatly in achieving that. One new clause which directly affects Breconshire is that which empowers local authorities in National Parks to make bye-laws prohibiting or restricting traffic on lakes in these areas. Legislation has already been prepared by the Breconshire County Council for Llangorse Lake, a habitat of tremendous biological importance which is being ruined by a 'free for all'. In 1954 the Nature Conservancy notified it as an S.S.S.I. and in the same year the County Council proposed to designate it as a Local Nature Reserve. In fifteen years no real progress has been possible. The ownership of the lake is still uncertain; there are twelve riparian owners. Its scientific importance is incontestable and was upheld at a Public Enquiry in 1968.

For many years Llangorse Lake has been famous for its wildlife. During the reign of Henry VIII Leland wrote of it 'On the one side wel nere the ripe is a kinde of weedes that goith alonge the Llin, wherin the spaune hath socur and also the great fische. . . . It berith as the principale fische a great number of bremes, and they appeyre in mightii sculles, so that sumtime they breke the nettes. . . . It berith also good pikes and perches in greate numbre. Trowtes also, and cheuyns by cumming in of Lleuenny'. In 1698 Edward Lhuyd, Keeper of the Ashmolean Museum at Oxford, perhaps better known to botanists as the discoverer of mountain spiderwort (*Lloydia serotina*) on Snowdon, described in a letter to a fellow antiquary in Yorkshire how he visited the 'Great lake called Llyn Savadhan' and discovered 'two elegant sorts of small leeches'. Once the booming of the bittern resounded around its reedy margins; a depressing list of records of bitterns shot at Llangorse at the turn of the century is given in 'The Birds of Brecknock'.

Even now, in spite of ever increasing pollution and disturbance from motor boats, the lake remains one of Breconshire's major habitats. Fine stands of the largest British buttercup, the greater spearwort (*Ranunculus lingua*), contrast with the deep purple spikes of loosestrife *(Lythrum salicaria)*, though some plants like the elegant pink flowering rush *(Butomus umbellatus)* are now perilously rare. Twenty-two species of flowering plants grow nowhere else in Breconshire except at the lake, and the luxurious aquatic and marsh plant communities provide the essential conditions of life for many rare insects and birds which breed there, like the water rail, sedge and reed warbler and great crested grebe. Pollution has increased greatly over the past five years and there are signs that it may have reached a critical level. Legislation is needed rapidly to save this important habitat for the sake of its wildlife and enjoyment of future generations.

One other Local Nature Reserve has been proposed by the County Council: Talybont reservoir, which is an important wildfowl refuge where some of the largest flocks of pochard in Wales may be seen in winter, in company with goosanders, tufted duck, golden eye, wigeon and mallard. This site is of considerable educational value, for visitors can watch the duck unobtrusively from the road alongside the reservoir.

In many places disused railway cuttings have become sanctuaries for wild flowers and butterflies. The Naturalists' Trust is at present negotiating to buy two of these sites. One is a stronghold of the green-winged orchid *(Orchis morio)* which has become very scarce here, as in other parts, by the upgrading of pastures with artificial fertilisers. The other has a limestone escarpment of geological interest and is the only 'station' in the county for bloody cranesbill *(Geranium sanguineum)*.

Hedgerows and roadside verges are also being surveyed for their wild life interest and four sites have so far been notified to the County Surveyor who has agreed to co-operate in protecting their inhabitants. Giant, nettle-leaved and spreading bellflowers *(Campanula latifolia, C. trachelium, C. patula)* are all occasionally found on the banks of lanes leading up to the Black Mountains and, as they bloom late in the summer, they have in many years been cut down by flail mowers before seeds set. Careful planning of cutting times can help to protect such plants. Fortunately, the Highways Department has shown considerable wisdom in its restriction of the use of weedkillers to pavement edges. But a careful watch needs to be kept, as improperly handled flail mowers, and herbicides sprayed along ditches, can have very harmful effects on wayside communities. Road verges which are a changing pageant of colourful wild flowers are not only more valuable to butterflies and birds but are also more aesthetically pleasing to the passing motorist than a monotonous strip of green grass.

Breconshire has about 151 000 acres of common land, the highest total for any county in Wales. Much of it is moorland and important ecologically in being the only extensive area of semi-natural vegetation, and often of great amenity value to walkers and pony-trekkers, and field centres and schools for field studies. The natural history of the smaller commons is being surveyed by the Trust so that it can be recorded at the appropriate stage of the Commons Registration Scheme. One exciting common contains a small moorland pool where pillwort *(Pilularia globulifera)*, orange foxtail, pennyroyal and floating marsh-wort *(Apium inundatum)* all grow.

Some of the hazards facing our countryside and its wildlife have been considered. Pressures are bound to increase as the population and tourist industry grow and more people come into the countryside for their leisure activities. The Naturalists' Trust has awakened to the urgency of the situation. Between its formation in 1964 and 1968 only one nature reserve, Ty-mawr pool, was established. However, in 1969 Craig-y-rhiwarth was designated and there are now a further eight reserves in the course of negotiation. It is hoped that several of these will be announced during 1970. But if the countryside is to survive the interest of all must be aroused, the local community and visitors alike, so that the need for its protection is understood, or to quote the Hobhouse report once more, the task is: 'To foster an intelligent public conscience, which will be more effective in the conservation of wildlife than any prohibitive regulations'.

PLATE 4. Female Kite at a nest in the Upper Towy Valley. From an old photograph taken by the late Arthur Brook in 1926.

XI

THE RED KITES OF WALES: THE STORY OF THEIR PRESERVATION

COLONEL H. MORREY SALMON, C.B.E., M.C., D.L., M.B.O.U.

Cardiff

BEFORE CONSIDERING why steps to preserve the Kite *(Milvus milvus)* as a breeding species in Wales became essential it is necessary to look briefly at the reasons why a widespread and relatively common bird virtually ceased to exist throughout almost the whole of Britain in the space of less than half a century, the first half of the nineteenth. Those who brought this about were the game-preserving landowners and their indiscriminate and destructive agents, the gamekeepers, who pursued their calling with a callous indifference for anything but game and an appalling amount of cruelty exercised with the connivance and, in some cases, the active participation of their masters. As the species became rarer it was the target for skin and egg collectors so that the last surviving isolated pairs in England and Scotland were exterminated in the 1870s.

In Wales it is doubtful whether kites bred even at all or at most very sparsely in the four northernmost counties and the northern areas of the other two. In southern Wales, however, it was common from Monmouthshire to, perhaps, the Pembrokeshire border until possibly the early 1830s, after which it vanished so rapidly that it was gone, as elsewhere, before anyone thought to record its disappearance. That a few pairs may have persisted is shown by the fact that a pair tried to breed in Leckwith Wood, Cardiff, in 1853; evidenced by the skin of the hen and her two eggs in a museum collection. By the middle of the second half of the nineteenth century the last few remaining kites were confined to central Wales, which was wild, mountainous and rugged, remote and sparsely populated; here the steep-sided valleys of the main and tributary rivers were still well-wooded, chiefly with mature if scrubby oaks, and provided a suitable habitat which extended from the Usk valley in Brecknock and the upper Towy (Tywi) in Carmarthenshire through Radnorshire and Cardiganshire to the southern fringes of Merioneth and Montgomeryshire.

Cambridge Phillips, in his first account in 1882 of the birds of his county, Breconshire, wrote that up to 1875 he had seen only two kites and considered them almost extinct, but in May of that year he saw his first kites' nest at Upper Chapel. Later, he recorded that during the next fourteen years up to 1889 kites had increased around Brecon and could often be seen over the town. About that time, however, Scottish gamekeepers were brought into the neighbouring estates and Cambridge Phillips recorded his great horror at hearing that no less than nine or ten kites had been killed by them in the spring of that year. Slaughter on this scale evidently aroused some landowners who, like Sir John Dillwyn-Llewelyn, had been endeavouring to protect kites on their estates and Cambridge Phillips noted that the Zoological Society of London had passed a special vote of thanks to them and to him. Ten years later, in the 1899 edition of his 'Birds of Breconshire', he wrote that kites were hardly holding their own but that a few pairs were still protected, as far as possible, in his county. This was, however, of little avail since in the Usk valley they had all succumbed to the gun and the egg-collector within ten years.

A little later than Cambridge Phillips in Breconshire, in the spring of 1893 Professor J. H. Salter first became acquainted with Welsh kites in the upper Towy valley in Carmarthenshire. Besides being Professor of Botany at Aberystwyth, Salter was also a competent field-ornithologist and recorded in the 'Zoologist' in August 1893 that he had seen two pairs and that others might have been found had time permitted but even then they had already been robbed of their eggs. There is sound evidence that kites had been breeding in this district about or just before 1860, so it seems likely that they had persisted there from the early years of the century.

It is curious that while both Cambridge Phillips and Salter were each writing to the 'Zoologist', overlapping each other, the former from 1882 onwards and the latter from 1893, they never seem to have made any mutual contact. Indeed, even later when, it is recorded, Cambridge Phillips was to be asked to collaborate with Salter, there is nothing to show that they did so; in fact, such evidence as there is suggests that they went their separate ways.

However, there is no question that it was Salter alone who took the initial step that brought into being an organisation for the protection of the Welsh kites which has continued for nearly seventy years in one form or another and, though several times perilously near to failure, has kept the kite as a British breeding bird.

Having for ten years seen the kites robbed annually of their eggs by collectors and many adult birds shot for their skins or to meet the craze for adorning country houses with cases of stuffed birds, on 13th February 1903 Salter addressed a letter to the British Ornithologists'

Club (B.O.C.) in an endeavour to enlist the sympathy of the members in the protection of the kites in Wales. This letter was read at a meeting of the Club on 18th February and Salter's plea was supported by the Rev. F. C. R. Jourdain, one of the most influential figures in British ornithological circles at that time. The upshot was that the thanks of the meeting were given to these two men for calling attention to the threatened extinction of the kite and the first 'Kite Committee' was brought into being, the founder-members being J. L. Bonhote, W. E. de Winton, E. G. B. Meade-Waldo, the Hon. W. Rothschild, M.P., Howard Saunders and Watkin Watkins. A fund was raised, £54 being subscribed or promised in the room. Others, like W. R. Ogilvie-Grant of the British Museum (N.H.) and H. F. Witherby became associated with the committee, the latter for a time as honorary secretary and treasurer, and some small disbursements to gain the co-operation of farmers and gamekeepers were made by Salter in 1904.

In January 1905 Meade-Waldo took over the treasurership of the kite fund and, although subscriptions to it were made by members at successive meetings of the Club up to at least 1918, the fund was, in fact, largely financed by Meade-Waldo himself and by one or two of his close friends. To what extent the Royal Society for the Protection of Birds (R.S.P.B.) was involved financially at this stage is not clear but there were suggestions that the Society might be asked to contribute £5 or £6 to the fund. It has to be remembered that Meade-Waldo was not only a notable figure in the British Ornithologists' Union (B.O.U.), of which he had been a member for twenty years, and of its off-shoot the B.O.C. but he was also an influential member of the R.S.P.B. Council and chairman of its Watchers' Committee. He was, in fact, chairman of the Watchers' Committee from its inception in 1904 until his death in 1934, with Mrs. F. E. Lemon as its honorary secretary throughout the same period.

The year 1905 was a notable one in kite history, since it was the year in which the newly founded Kite Committee was able to record its first success but it was also a year in respect of which there is great confusion in the records of the kite population. In his letter to the B.O.C. of 13th February 1903 Salter stated that the kites were restricted to a 'very limited district in South Wales' and, while it was difficult to estimate their numbers, there were 'certainly three, and probably five or six pairs — eight would be the outside limit'. It is possible that he had the whole of the South Wales area in mind, since he referred to Breconshire indirectly, but other points suggest that he meant only the Towy valley. Only four months afterwards, in June 1903, he wrote to the 'Zoologist' that kites in Wales were reduced to two or three pairs, which suggests he was then thinking of the upper

Towy, the only area he really knew anything about in those days. Later again, Meade-Waldo claimed that kites in 1905 were reduced to two pairs and one odd bird and this, unfortunately, was repeated by Witherby in several publications up to and including vol. III of the 'Handbook of British Birds' in 1939.

This was quite at variance with the information given to Meade-Waldo by Salter at the time and the writer corrected it in 1957, showing that there must have been at least nine and probably twelve kites in existence in that year (1905).

However, on 1st June 1905 Lord Cawdor wrote to Ogilvie-Grant that two pairs of kites had nested on his land in Carmarthenshire and, though one had been raided, presumably by egg-collectors, the other nest held two young about a fortnight old. Three weeks later Salter wrote to Meade-Waldo to tell him that, in addition, a third nest also held two young, nearly ready to fly.

Just before this, Salter had introduced Meade-Waldo to the Rev. D. Edmondes Owen, then Rector of Llanelwedd in Radnorshire and afterwards vicar of Llandovery, who played a vital role in the efforts to protect Welsh kites for the next seventeen years.

Salter had suggested that Meade-Waldo should visit the area to become acquainted with the problems and said that Edmondes Owen would entertain him and would 'prove an able and obliging guide'. Meade-Waldo did go to Wales where he met Alfred Gwynne-Vaughan of Builth Wells, son of Henry Gwynne-Vaughan, D.L., J.P., the Squire of Cynghordy in Carmarthenshire. Gwynne-Vaughan played a considerable part in kite matters with Edmondes Owen for a number of years. After Meade-Waldo had returned Edmondes Owen wrote to him 'Your visit was an encouragement and an inspiration. We are all so glad that you were able to see the young birds in both nests. Dr Salter, Mr Gwynne-Vaughan and I realise more than ever how hopeless the task of protecting the kites would be without the sympathy and support of the B.O.C. and of the Earl of Cawdor'. Salter expressed the belief that these were the first young kites reared for ten years.

In the following year, 1906, three young in a Towy valley nest were photographed by Richard Kearton and these later flew safely. In the Usk valley one pair nested and reared two young which were, however, shot in the following December. Next year these south Breconshire birds were robbed of their eggs, so it is recorded, by a party who travelled from London by car; there is no record that they ever nested again, though they may have persisted in the district until perhaps 1909.

Other pairs were becoming known outside the Towy area but they did not have much success. As many as eight nests were known at one time and in 1910 five young were reared and in 1911 three. The year 1912 was a record one, however, for ten pairs were known, of which nine nested and reared eight young successfully, in spite of three nests being destroyed. The tenth pair may also have successfully reared one young bird. Meade-Waldo wrote that this great success was due to Edmondes Owen, Gwynne-Vaughan and Colonel Drummond, Lord Cawdor's agent.

In contrast, 1913 was a year of total failure and in 1914 only two young were reared. The war years that followed proved extremely difficult and so did those of the immediate post-war period; few young had been reared and, in fact, 1920 was referred to by Salter as 'a year of disaster'. Government timber-cutting was being carried out on a large scale with consequent disturbance of the kites; many of the men employed on this work carried guns and a number of kites were shot; there was a recrudescence of egg-collecting, often done by local men acting for principals away from the area.

In 1922 Edmondes Owen was clearly very pessimistic, writing to Meade-Waldo that there were fewer kites than for thirteen years; three pairs, he suggested, being 'the whole remnant'. However, as the breeding season progressed he became a little more optimistic, though there was little success and he was most disheartened when a normally safe nest was deserted due to an attempt to photograph the kites by a well-known bird-photographer, with full permission of all concerned. Shortly afterwards Edmondes Owen died in August of that year.

Meade-Waldo, of course, needed a successor and apparently decided to ask the Rev. W. J. Constable, then living in the Towy valley a couple of miles below the village of Cilycwm, to carry on the work. Constable had been a house-master at a well-known public school and had come to the area about six years earlier. Obviously he had more than a passing interest in the birds and clearly Meade-Waldo had become acquainted with him when visiting Edmondes Owen so that, though at first reluctant, he eventually agreed.

At this time and for the first time the Royal Society for the Protection of Birds became directly involved in the actual protective work amongst the Welsh kites. Salter and Edmondes Owen had worked out a scheme under which farmers and others on whose land a pair successfully reared young were paid a reward, at first £5, later £8 and eventually £10; also, at some vulnerable nests, local watchers were employed during critical periods and were, of course, paid. This system aroused many jealousies and there were even cases of nests being destroyed out of spite. Nevertheless, it was probably the best way at the time and Constable said that the local large landowners and he himself were in favour of continuing it.

The rewards due for Edmondes Owen's last year were outstanding when he died and these were paid by Mrs. F. E. Lemon on behalf of the Watchers Committee of the R.S.P.B. on such information as she could obtain and on a quite generous scale.

Mrs. Lemon was a strong-willed personality who would admit no other view but her own; she was a founder-member of the Society in 1889 and had been its honorary secretary for ten years until her husband succeeded her in that office and she became honorary secretary of the Watchers Committee at its inception in 1904, a position she held until she officially retired, nearing her 80th year, in 1939. She epitomised the R.S.P.B. of her day; intolerant, prejudiced, with narrow concepts far removed from the broad-minded, tolerant and far-seeing institution it is today, but she served it well according to her tenets. Nevertheless, her attitude did not help the kites since, out of prejudice against a landowner who was known to be an egg-collector in a quite small way but of considerable influence in Brecon-shire and who would have been most helpful, she abandoned the kites breeding in an adjacent part of that county and encouraged Constable to have nothing to do with them, so that the latter super-vised only his own immediate district.

In Constable's first year three young kites were reared but for his second he had to record, disconsolately, 'this year of failure'; the only nest with young had been maliciously destroyed at a late stage. He advised Meade-Waldo not to come down as he had nothing to show, much to the latter's dissatisfaction.

At the end of his report he said he had been much helped by a retired police-inspector, Mr A. W. Jones, and recommended that he be employed by the R.S.P.B. in a supervisory capacity at an honorarium of £10 per annum. This was agreed and Jones played a considerable and active part in kite matters for many years afterwards. There was clearly a need for someone to keep in touch with breeding kites and with farmers on whose land they nested, because Constable had an extraordinary mentality and seemed imbued with the need for pro-found secrecy, even to the extent of trying to keep Inspector Jones in complete ignorance of any nest a little removed from the latter's immediate district around Rhandirmwyn where he lived and all com-munications with Jones and with gamekeepers and farmers, even in Constable's most immediate neighbourhood at Cilycwm, were carried on by letter through the post. He even went so far as to remonstrate with Salter for visiting the area during the kites' breeding season!

How ineffective were his methods is exemplified by the fact that the photograph of a kite at its nest which illustrates this article was taken after a quite open approach to a well known nest-site by the late Arthur Brook, with the help of Captain H. A. Gilbert, in 1926. Afterwards, the hen was seen to return to her nest and young before

Brook and Gilbert left the area and a fortnight later Constable wrote to Meade-Waldo that the hen was still feeding young in this nest, though the cock had not been seen for some days (Plate 4).

Breeding success was negligible in several years, often only one or two young being brought to the flying stage; the best was in 1929 when there were five. Meade-Waldo had been unable to visit Wales owing to ill-health for several years before his death, in his 80th year, in 1934 and there were several untoward incidents which caused him to write to Salter in 1932 referring to 'these last three disastrous years'. In 1931 Mrs. Lemon had written direct to Inspector Jones, by-passing Constable, asking his candid opinion whether it was worthwhile continuing to try to save the kites; Jones temporised and suggested deferring any decision in the hope of better things next year but soon Constable was also asking himself and Mrs. Lemon the same question.

There had long been suspicion that, with the connivance of some of the watchers, kites' eggs were being taken and buzzards' eggs broken in the nest to suggest that they had been eaten by crows; the village policeman in Cilycwm tried to sell a kite's egg to a visitor; finally, much to Inspector Jones's chagrin, one of his trusted watchers was caught attempting to sell a clutch of three eggs taken in this manner.

The incident which had the widest repercussions, however, occurred in 1932 when a clutch of eggs taken from one of Constable's nests in 1930 by a young, then relatively unknown, collector was exhibited at a meeting of the British Oologists' Association. The reverberations of this affair, which led to many resignations from this Association, went on for nearly three years, with discussions amongst leading British ornithologists which almost led to the formation of yet another 'Kite Committee'.

Meanwhile, there were rumblings of discontent within the R.S.P.B. directed at the high-handed methods of Mrs. Lemon and, inside and outside the Society, there was strong criticism of Constable's methods which were regarded as inept and useless. Up to 1933 Mrs. Lemon had insisted upon a policy of complete secrecy but she was over-ruled and at the end of that year it was decided to make a wide public appeal to save the kites. This took the form of an eight page leaflet with a statement by Dr P. R. Lowe, British Museum (N.H.) and an appeal to all, landowners, farmers, gamekeepers and shooting men generally, to spare the bird, signed by the Presidents of the R.S.P.B., C.P.R.E., C.P.R.W. and B.O.U., chairman B.O.C. and the Lords Lieutenant of the several Welsh counties concerned.

At about this time moves to replace Constable were begun and, with the support of some members of the R.S.P.B. Council, Miss D. T. Raikes of Bwlch, Breconshire, began to visit the Towy area and the kites' breeding quarters there; so much so that by 1937 there were two local kite-protection organisations, side-by-side and, indeed, over-lapping in some instances. Mrs Lemon complained bitterly that nearly £200 of R.S.P.B. money had been spent in that year with only one young kite reared to show for it. Miss Raikes did, however, spread her net much wider than the Towy valley, visiting areas such as Radnor Forest where kites formerly nested and had been seen more recently, although Constable had, in fact, obtained information from here several years earlier through the then Conservator, Forestry Commission.

After the end of the 1937 breeding season Constable, disappointed and despondent, decided to retire; he had worked for the R.S.P.B. for fourteen years to the best of his ability in this field and was approaching his 80th year. The Society awarded him its Silver Medal but, in the event, he could not bring himself to go to receive it in person. Mrs. Lemon, similarly near to her 80th year, frustrated and embittered, retired in the following year, though officially remaining in office until 1939.

Miss Raikes was appointed by the R.S.P.B. Council to take over from Constable and was granted £100 towards expenses in 1938. Clearly, however, she intended to and, in fact, did set up an organisation entirely independent of the R.S.P.B. and at the end of 1937 sent out a widely-circulated appeal for funds, as she envisaged spending much more than the £100 from the R.S.P.B. In fact, £340 was spent in 1938 upon five known pairs in the Towy area for a total increment of one kite reared to the flying stage. Later in that year a claim was made that a sixth pair had bred in a district described as 'west Herefordshire' on the basis of a report that three kites had been seen together in August-September, of which two were believed to have been young birds of the year.

Miss Raikes' next report, for the year 1939, was circulated some time in the following year when the writer was away on active service but eventually he received a copy. Six pairs were known at the beginning of the breeding season but, in the event, again only one young kite was reared in the Towy area after the expenditure of over £410, of which the R.S.P.B. provided £100. Another pair was reported by a farmer thirty miles to the north and on his word two more young reared were claimed.

During the war years travelling became more and more difficult so that Miss Raikes could make only occasional visits to the kite country. Fortunately, for her, however, Mrs. I. M. Vaughan at Rhandirmwyn, though primarily a botanist, interested herself in the welfare of the kites and throughout the war years carried out the greater part of the work of locating nesting pairs and verifying results. Commander (later Captain) H. R. H. and Mrs. Vaughan had come to reside at Rhandirmwyn in 1938, though he was away on active service in the Royal Navy until the end of the war, and Miss Raikes acknowledged that, but for their kindness in allowing her to be at their house on her visits to the Towy area she would have been unable to do any kite work at all.

Extremely little is known of what happened in the five years 1940-1944; Miss Raikes made no further reports, though in 1944 she did make another appeal for funds; the R.S.P.B. continued to provide £100, later reduced to £50, annually. Not more than five pairs were known in any of these years and an aggregate of possibly fourteen young kites flew. All watching of nests had been discontinued and reliance placed upon paying farmers a £20 reward for a successful nest on their land.

In 1945, just after the end of the war in Europe, some members of the R.S.P.B. Council, accompanied by Miss Raikes, visited the Towy area; they were told there were possibly five pairs and had been four nests, two of which then held four young kites almost ready to fly. Thus, forty years later, the young birds reared were the same as in 1905, with virtually the same number of known pairs; hardly a successful outcome of so much toil and expenditure.

This virtually ended Miss Raikes' period, since in the following years up to 1948 she was incapacitated and did not visit the area, though she continued to hold the funds and wrote about kites to the R.S.P.B. perhaps once or twice a year on information communicated to her by Mrs. Vaughan.

Visits were paid in 1946-1947 again by members of the R.S.P.B. Council but the whole burden in the Towy area was being carried by Mrs. Vaughan. With the war ended and somewhat greater freedom to move about, other pairs were found beyond the restricted area looked after in wartime and at least six or seven pairs became known hereabouts. Not only so, but pairs with nests and young were discovered in 1946 and 1947 in north Cardiganshire.

It had been the fashion to refer to these far outlying kites as being in ' colony areas ', with the suggestion that they had been occupied by surplus young birds reared in the ' central area ' of upper Towy. In the writer's view this was completely mistaken. Of course, these kites must have come from somewhere but they were being reported in the 1930s at a time when, as now, there were hardly enough young being reared in the Towy area to replace normal wastage, much less to reoccupy distant parts. It is his considered opinion that kites, probably several pairs, had been nesting with some success through these years, scattered over this area of several hundred square miles, unnoticed and unrecorded. That this could have happened is exemplified by recent experience in the 1960s when, in spite of much more intensive searching than in the earlier years, breeding pairs have been found only after they had been in occupation of a site for even two or three years.

Captain Vaughan retired from the Royal Navy at the end of the war and, with Mrs. Vaughan, took an increasing interest in the organisation of kite conservation; in fact, they were carrying the whole burden, since Miss Raikes was still incapacitated. In 1949 the position became so difficult that Captain Vaughan took the step of proposing to the Council of the West Wales Field Society that they should take over the whole organisation and a sub-committee of the Society, with representation of the R.S.P.B., was brought into being. This sub-committee presented its report for the year 1949 to a special meeting of the W.W.F.S. Council, to which had been invited representatives of a number of other like-minded bodies, and it was learned that of the Towy area pairs only three were known to have bred, rearing four young, and from the only other known nest in north Cardiganshire the two young kites unaccountably disappeared when about three weeks old. At the end of 1949 the winter kite population of central Wales was estimated at a total of twenty-four birds.

This meeting took the important step of setting up a body designated the 'Kite Committee', composed initially of representatives of W.W.F.S. and of R.S.P.B., S.P.N.R., C.P.R.W. and the Cardiff Naturalists' Society, with Captain Vaughan as chairman, to organise and co-ordinate all steps practicable for the conservation of kites in Wales. Miss Raikes was invited to join the committee but did not accept.

The results of the next five years 1950-1954 have been summarised by the writer (*British Birds*, April 1957) and it is unnecessary to detail them here, but the success of the new approach to the problem may be gauged by the numbers of young kites to reach the flying stage: in 1950 — eight; in 1951 — ten; in 1952 — six; in 1953 — ten; in 1954 — fifteen, the highest number in any year in this century.

In 1954 twelve pairs nested out of fifteen pairs known definitely, with the possibility of three other pairs and some unattached birds, and at the end of that breeding season the estimated total kite population was fifty-five birds, which indicates fairly high unexplained losses over the five year period.

Unfortunately, during this period also, stresses and strains within the committee became apparent, mainly because of the actions of certain individuals in some of the organisations involved, remote from the actual work of conservation in the field, who tried to influence the work of the committee into directions which those most closely connected with the actual work in the field considered would not be in the interest of the birds themselves. In the end this led to a complete break between those working in the field and the two main sponsoring Societies, the last meeting of the committee being held in 1955.

Just after the end of the extraordinarily successful, record breeding season of 1954 disaster struck the kites, and other raptorial birds as well, when myxomatosis virtually wiped out the whole rabbit population of the country. Followed as this was by a long, cold and wet winter the kites fared badly and in the 1955 breeding season possibly ten pairs tried to nest and of these perhaps four may have had eggs; only one single young bird flew. The year 1956 was little better with only eight pairs located and three young birds reared but in 1957 there was a slight improvement and six young kites reached the flying stage.

The breakdown of the Kite Committee was regrettable but it did not stop the conservation work which was carried on by Captain and Mrs. Vaughan with their small band of devoted field-workers. Meanwhile, for two years the writer tried in vain to bring together the opposing parties within the moribund Kite Committee; finally in January 1958 an acceptable formula was devised and, largely through the good offices of Lord Hurcomb, a meeting of the committee was convened two months later in March 1958.

Lord Hurcomb took the chair and in his opening remarks said that the R.S.P.B. was only too anxious to extend its help towards the protection of the kites as it did with other rare species in Britain and that the appointment of a Regional Officer by the Nature Conservancy, who would include in his duties research into the ecology of the kite, constituted a new circumstance relevant to the question whether it was necessary any longer to maintain this special committee of the West Wales Field Society. The writer proposed that the committee be dissolved, funds held by W.W.F.S. be transferred to R.S.P.B. and the latter to accept responsibility for special measures in relation to the kite as they did with other rare birds. This was agreed and so began yet another new chapter in the story of the survival of the kite in Wales. The writer paid tribute to the W.W.F.S. which at that time, at least, had done more nature conservation in Wales than all other societies together and to the R.S.P.B. which, in spite of many differences of view from time to time, had always met the agreed financial commitments incurred in kite conservation.

During the breeding season which followed the small group of field-workers who had co-operated with Captain and Mrs. Vaughan continued, with them, to look after the kites in their several areas. They were heartened in their task by the knowledge that now they had the full co-operation of the R.S.P.B.; a new, forward-looking, broad-minded body so different from the old Society of narrow outlook and short-sighted policies. Particularly welcome was Mr P. J. Conder, then Reserves Manager, who kept closely in touch with Captain Vaughan throughout that first year of the new regime. In the autumn they met at Rhandirmwyn, to enjoy Mrs. Vaughan's gracious hospitality and to discuss the results of the year so that they might be evaluated and chronicled, successes and failures analysed, rewards assessed and problems and policy debated. Thus, in 1958, in a so very informal way the 'Kite Committee' came back into being, although not under that designation; in fact, it has never since had a formal title!

That year was not a good one; from twelve nesting pairs only five young birds flew and it was heart-breaking that one even of these was found in the autumn dying from a *pasteurella* infection.

The years 1959 and 1960 were better, with eight and ten young flying respectively, but 1961 was disappointing with a high proportion of failures and only six young reared; 1962 raised high hopes with fifteen nests but fulfilment did not come, eight young being reared from only six nests.

The year 1963 proved even worse; only three pairs, out of fourteen nesting, reared but four young birds. Clearly some new factor was involved and the clue to this came when a kite, picked up dead after the severe weather in the early months of 1963, was found on analysis to contain a very high content of dieldrin, one of the notorious agricultural chemicals of the persistent chlorinated-hydrocarbon group. There have always been some inexplicable failures but here was a steeply rising incidence from two in 1960 to eleven in 1963, coinciding exactly with the introduction and use of this poison for sheep-dipping on a widespread scale in the area.

The year 1964 was little better with only seven young kites reared but since then there has been an improvement; in 1965 eleven young flew, at that time the second highest total in any year in this century. This was equalled in 1967, with only one less in 1966 and in both years possibly twenty pairs began nest building. In 1968 from a similar number of nests twelve young fledged, though one was found dead in the autumn, having flown into telephone wires. In 1969 there were twenty-two nests and fourteen young fledged but again one was early found dead, probably from eating a mole poisoned with strychnine. A very noteworthy fact in 1969 was the rearing to the flying stage of two broods each of three young; this has not happened since 1912 and may be a pointer to young and virile stock in the area.

Nevertheless, several disturbing factors have to be noted. Firstly, still every year at least one clutch of eggs disappears under circumstances suggesting that egg-collectors have been responsible; secondly, there has again become evident the taking from nests of young birds at an advanced stage, presumably to fill the demand brought about by the increase of keeping birds of prey in captivity, privately or in the many so-called 'wildlife parks' that are springing up all over the country; thirdly, there may be the residual and probably cumulative effects of these persistent toxic chemicals which, in the writer's opinion, are still being felt in the southern part of the kites' range, where the proportion of eggs failing to hatch or of young dying in the first week or so after hatching has long been and still is very high. Possibly here there may be, also, a number of ageing individual birds in the population.

Over the past twenty years there have been sporadic excursions by single pairs to districts well outside the present occupied area, extended as this now is, though these have not yet resulted in permanent re-occupation of former haunts, but if present progress is continued this may come in time.

We now have in Wales a kite population of approaching seventy birds but there is no room for complacency; a combination of two or more adverse circumstances, as in 1954 or 1963, might bring about a major reverse.

Since the present group of field-workers under Captain Vaughan's chairmanship met in 1958 those who have taken part have come together each year after the breeding season and have been joined by Peter Conder, David Lea and others of the R.S.P.B. in a most cordial and pleasant relationship, carrying on this voluntary task of conservation in which many frustrations and disappointments have had to be set off against a measure of relatively small but gratifying success. Most cordial relations and co-operation, too, have been experienced with the Nature Conservancy and the Forestry Commission though on, perhaps, the somewhat more formal basis that befits dealings with government departments. The assistance given by officers, wardens, foresters and others of both bodies has been invaluable. A transfer of more direct responsibility to the R.S.P.B. and the Nature Conservancy, a process already begun, is inevitable. Finally, most important of all, gratitude must be expressed for the co-operation of those landowners and farmers on whose terrain kites have nested over the years.

By the time this appears in print it will be fifty years since the writer first saw Welsh kites in their native haunts and this paper is based on his own experiences, including those gained as recorded over the past twenty years; on personal knowledge of almost all the personalities who have been involved and, as well, amplified by much information from many sources which he gratefully acknowledges.

XII

THE ISLAND RESERVES OF WALES

R. M. LOCKLEY

West Wales Naturalists' Trust

OMITTING THE LARGEST ISLAND OF ALL, Anglesey, and its satellite Holy Island, both now in effect made peninsular by the road-rail links with the mainland, there are a dozen true islands upwards of ten acres in extent, as well as some smaller islets, off the coast of Wales. All of them, fortunately, are pleasant refuges where wildlife is conserved by their owners or occupiers, or both. Happily, too, of these at least eight are declared or recognised Nature Reserves.

We may begin our tour of these in the south-west, where the West Wales Naturalists' Trust (then the Pembrokeshire Bird Protection Society) was early in the field of island conservation, and now controls five interesting reserves: Skokholm, Skomer, Grassholm, St. Margaret's and Cardigan Islands (Plate 5).

SKOKHOLM

240 acres, privately owned, leased to the W.W.N.T. 5 miles W. of St. Ann's Head, S.W. Pembrokeshire.

The first Bird Observatory in the British Isles was established here in 1933 during the writer's lease of this exposed, treeless, wind and tide-swept Atlantic island. Of a rich-coloured Old Red sandstone, the island is small enough for most birds which visit it to be seen and recorded easily. Ring-marking of these migrants and of the huge population of nesting shearwaters, petrels, auks, gulls and other sea-birds has been a major task of the Observatory, and has produced valuable scientific results in monographs and migration studies; and proved a hitherto unsuspected regular passage of species formerly thought to be rare visitors. More birds have been ringed here annually than anywhere else in the British Isles. The colony of about one thousand pairs of storm petrels is one of the largest known.

The publication of many papers on the plant and animal ecology of the island suggests that it may now be one of the most studied of small islands of its size in the world. Even so there is much more to be learned, as ever in scientific field studies; those interested should apply to the W.W.N.T. for details of accommodation. The resident warden is available to advise and help amateur and professional alike.

SKOMER

722 acres, 2 miles N. of Skokholm, a National Nature Reserve, leased to the W.W.N.T.

For its size and number of nesting species this is possibly the finest sea-bird reserve in the British Isles. A largely rock-bound basaltic plateau, it rises to a central height of 228 ft, with a splendid cliff scenery. Apart from some damage done during the 'black era' of rabbit gin-trapping in Wales 1900-50, resulting in the maiming and death of many birds, including buzzards, ravens, choughs, oyster-catchers and other species, Skomer has been more or less a sanctuary for wildlife since it was abandoned as a farm at the end of the last century. In 1959 it was purchased by agreement between the Nature Conservancy and the West Wales Naturalists' Trust, the latter raising £4000 and the Conservancy £6000 of the purchase price. This was a model arrangement between a government department and a voluntary body, enabling the Conservancy to become the owner and provide the security of a National Nature Reserve, as well as a new house and work laboratory. This was built in a strategic position over-looking the north and south landing havens, and is occupied by a warden maintained by the Trust as lessee. A landing fee of 5s (payable by non-members of the Trust) helps towards the salary of the warden. There is simple chalet accommodation in the old farm buildings for naturalists wishing to study the rich bird life, mammals, invertebrates, marine biology, and the striking floral sequence and maritime plants. Mammals include the unique bank vole *(Clethrionomys skomerensis)*, field mouse *(Apodemus sylvaticus)*, common and pygmy shrews, rabbit; and a herd of grey seals producing about fifty pups each autumn. Manx shearwaters are estimated at some 50 000 pairs, puffins about half this figure, about 4000 pairs of gulls of four species, and probably 2000 pairs each of razorbills and guillemots. Among some two dozen land birds breeding are raven, chough, short-eared owl, buzzard and (irregularly) peregrine falcon. For the archaeologist there is considerable evidence of human occupation of the Iron Age period in a series of early field systems and associated enclosures, including a promontory fort, remains of houses and water-dams.

MIDDLEHOLM

21·5 acres, a private uninhabited reserve, lies 80 yards east of Skomer and 624 yards from the S.W. mainland of Pembrokeshire across Jack Sound. Rock types, fauna and flora are similar to those of Skomer.

GRASSHOLM

22 acres, seven miles W. of Skomer, purchased in 1947 by the Royal Society for the Protection of Birds: custody given to W.W.N.T.

Geologically of the same basaltic rock-type as Skomer. Inaccessible for landing except in very calm weather. In 1860, after long exploitation by fishermen and others, there were only twenty pairs of gannets nesting, although traces of ancient stone compounds suggest that centuries earlier (possibly Iron Age) these and other large edible sea birds were harvested for food. After 1860 protection under private ownership was intermittent up to about 1924, when it is estimated that 1000 pairs of gannets were present. There was a rapid increase to about 5000 nests by 1933, 10 000 by 1956, and over 15 000 by 1969. In the same period of a hundred years there have been other population changes, notably of seals and puffins, discussed later (THE CHANGING ECOLOGY, *p.* 86). There is no habitation or water on this islet.

RAMSEY

600 acres, 2 miles S.W. of St. David's Head. National Trust Covenant. managed as a Reserve by the R.S.P.B.

Scenically a very striking island, with two hills rising to 446 ft and 323 ft, almost sheer on the exposed western coast. For centuries it has been farmed with crops and stock, but with mixed success, the main discouragement of late years having been the difficulty of controlling rabbits and rats. Probably the rats have been responsible for the disappearance of puffins and shearwaters, said to have been numerous two hundred years ago. Its main attractions today are the rugged rock and cliff exposures which provide nesting sites safe from man and rat for gulls, razorbills, guillemots, fulmars, choughs, ravens, buzzards, occasionally peregrine falcons; also the numerous deep caves and pebble beaches accommodating a large herd of grey seals, where each autumn about 200 pups are born. The island's position at the southern entrance to the Irish Sea is ideal for observing bird migration.

PLATE 5. ISLAND RESERVES. *Above*, Skokholm, privately owned and leased to the West Wales Naturalists' Trust as a Nature Reserve. The first island Bird Observatory in the British Isles was established here. *Below*, Grassholm, owned by the Royal Society for the Protection of Birds and managed by the West Wales Naturalists' Trust. Noted for its large gannetry.

PLATE 6. *Above*, little terns in one of only about six sites in Wales where the species still breeds. This and other shore-nesting birds are suffering increasingly from human disturbance. *Below*, common guillemots on cliff ledges at Trwyn Ciian, Lleyn, Caernarvonshire. One of the many species of auks badly affected by oil pollution at sea.

There is a resident warden; and hostel-type accommodation available on application to the R.S.P.B.

CALDY

About 500 acres, near Tenby, owned by the Cistercian community.

Possibly the fairest island of Wales, with its warm climate, wooded enclosures and Mediterranean appearance of the wide-eaved turreted monastic settlement. Geologically the island exhibits high cliffs of both Carboniferous limestone and Old Red sandstone. There are many caves in the limestone, which have yielded Neolithic flint tools and the bones of woolly rhinoceros, mammoth, reindeer, musk ox, cave bear and other animals contemporary with Neanderthal man. The main plateau of the island is a fertile farm, well cared for by the Cistercian brothers, who also protect all wildlife except agricultural pests. From Tenby pier a shuttle boat service conveys day-visitors, except Sundays and after 6 p.m. Most of the island coast is accessible to visitors, except the wooded sanctuary. The limestone flora is specially interesting and there are cliff-nesting birds. At low spring tides it is possible to scramble along the rock shore to reach St. Margaret's Island.

ST MARGARET'S ISLAND

Under 20 acres, leased by the W.W.N.T.

Entirely Carboniferous limestone, formerly much quarried, so much so that the walls of a religious cell, now roofless, stand on the edge of the excavated cliffs which are inhabited by more than fifty pairs of cormorants, perhaps the largest colony in Wales. Other nesting sea-birds include shag, razorbill, guillemot, kittiwake and other gulls. The few pairs of puffins are confined to niches in the cliffs secure from the brown rats, which are all too numerous. This is one of the few protected colonies of cormorants, an otherwise unprotected bird. Marking has shown that the St Margaret's cormorants disperse on a southerly migration in the autumn, when a very high proportion is killed by fishermen and water-bailiffs as they raid trout rivers and lakes.
Permits to visit St Margaret's from W.W.N.T.

FLATHOLM

52 acres, owned by Trinity House, lies about 12 miles south of Cardiff in the Bristol Channel fairway. Part of Glamorgan.

A low Carboniferous islet with a lighthouse, it has been at various times a farm, an isolation hospital, a garrison, and a pilot station with an inn. Most of the buildings are now derelict and uninhabited. The islet's position suggests that it would make a good station for observing cross-channel bird and insect migration. At present there is a colony of shelducks nesting in the numerous rabbit burrows; and a rapidly increasing population of herring and lesser black-backed gulls (approaching 2000 nesting pairs in 1969).

CARDIGAN ISLAND

About 40 acres, at the mouth of the Teifi estuary, is the property of the W.W.N.T.

Formerly held a large colony of puffins, which has dwindled away completely, possibly hastened by the arrival of brown rats with the wreck of the 7000 ton liner *Herefordshire* on tow, which went aground on Cardigan Island in 1934. There is a strong cormorant and shag colony on the sedimentary cliffs of this grassy islet, and choughs are common, although no nest has yet been found in several likely cave crannies. The Trust maintains a flock of the Soay or Viking sheep. Grey seals are resident along the shore, daily hauling out on the low-water rocks. Recently the Trust has, it is believed, exterminated the rats.

BARDSEY

444 acres, two miles south of the tip of Lleyn peninsula of Caernarvonshire, a privately owned reserve.

Scenically most attractive, with a gorse and bracken-clothed hill 548 ft. high on the east side, which screens the low western portion containing some dozen farmhouses, mostly in semi-detached pairs, and well over a hundred tiny fields; and at the south end a lighthouse. Famous as the site of an early Celtic monastic cell, founded about AD 420. Subsequently St Mary's Abbey, built about AD 516, became a place of pilgrimage and burial (20 000 saints, martyrs and holy confessors are said to have been buried there!). All that remains of the once

84

large monastic settlement is a portion of the thirteenth century tower built by the Augustinian Canons. When the writer first visited Bardsey in 1934 the farmhouses were occupied by some forty Welsh-speaking islanders, a fairly new colonization following the departure in 1926 of an older group under the patriarchal Love Pritchard, who was the last so-called King of Bardsey (a title first created by the landlord, Lord Newborough, in 1874, who presented a crown of tin for the purpose). This had been the pattern of tenancies for many decades — the older generation migrating to the mainland after saving money by working hard at their smallholdings and the lobster-fishing. But the sequence was broken during the second world war, after which the isolation and difficulty of making a profit on the very small farms has led to an amalgamation of holdings in the hands of the few who are prepared to face the isolation. The reversion of much of the farmland grazing has had its advantages for the visiting naturalist: the more Bardsey returns to wilderness the more attractive it is to wildlife. For instance, with less farming pressure, Manx shearwaters have increased tenfold from a few hundred to about three thousand pairs, spreading from their old colonies on the high land to the dilapidated rabbit-invaded field boundaries.

In 1953 the present Bird and Field Observatory was set up in the farmhouse of Cristin by a co-operative effort of the West Wales Naturalists' Trust, and the West Midland Bird Club, later joined by the North Wales Naturalists' Trust. Simple hostel accommodation is available, and there is a warden resident from March to October inclusive. The annual reports of the Observatory cover many branches of natural science; the geology, plants, animals and marine life provide new fields for study. The emphasis is on birds: several thousand are ringed each year, many caught in the fixed and movable nets, and on misty nights at the lighthouse; and, as at Skokholm, some migrants hitherto thought to be rare and accidental have proved regular visitors. There have been some species of American origin recorded at Bardsey which are new to Britain. Among several cliff-nesting species four pairs of choughs normally breed.

YNYS GWYLAN FAWR AND FACH

Two small grassy rocky islets off Aberdaron, Caerns. Uninhabited; records made by Bardsey Observatory. Small colonies of puffin, guillemot, razorbill, cormorant, shag, lesser black-backed and about 1000 pairs of herring gulls.

ST TUDWAL'S ISLES

2½ miles S.E. of Abersoch, Caerns. Privately owned, two small islets each a few acres in extent. Some remains of a monastic cell. Herring gulls are numerous but the wildlife has been impoverished by resident rats.

SKERRIES

A low group of very small islets and bare rocks 2½ miles N.W. of Carmel Head, Anglesey. Trinity House maintains the lighthouse there. A few sea birds, including terns and gulls, nest; and grey seals bask and fish regularly — occasionally a pup is born there.

PUFFIN ISLAND

Also known as Priestholm and Ynys Seiriol, about 70 acres, off the easterly point of Anglesey. Privately owned. Of Carboniferous limestone, rising to 193 ft.

So called because it once swarmed with puffins, now much diminished, due to the presence of brown rats. Its other names are associated with St Seiriol, a hermit who built a cell on the island about AD 540. The present remains and tower are late Norman, relics of the medieval monastery, which was a place of pilgrimage in the Middle Ages.

Of recent years rabbits have been decimated by myxomatosis, with consequent changes in the floral communities, and the growth of tall plants, among which many gulls continue to nest. The flora has always provided a main interest, having been recorded at least as far back as Ray's visit in 1662. Cormorants, shags, guillemots, razorbills and kittewakes nest in the low cliffs.

THE CHANGING ECOLOGY

To the naturalist small islands have an interest out of proportion to their size; there is an added satisfaction in studying island-living species of animals and plants, not only because some are slightly different, perhaps subspecific, but because one is ever aware of the definite, yet infinite, boundary of ocean limiting the range of those individuals confined within this physical, beautiful barrier. Basically the flora of small islands is conditioned by their climate and geological structure; but as the thumbnail sketches of Welsh islands in this article have shown, the influence of man and other mammals in considerable, notably the effects of grazing by rabbits and other herbivores, and the presence of rats which are omnivorous. Rats, especially the brown rat *(Rattus norvegicus)* which arrived in Wales in the middle of the eighteenth century, have caused great changes in the populations of burrowing sea birds on islands to which they have gained access. But other changes in the last hundred years have not been caused by rabbits or rats: some have been due to conservation provided by man, some to natural causes. There is room here to refer to only a few of the more spectacular of these changes.

The increase of gannets at Grassholm under protection has already been described. In the same period grey seals have also greatly multiplied. J. J. Neale saw only one in 1890 at Grassholm; by 1956 it was possible to count 120 basking there over low tide, as it still is today. Absolute protection of seals at their main nurseries of Skomer and Ramsey has resulted in an increase from a few isolated pairs in remote caves to the present herd of about 2000, producing possibly around 500 pups along all coasts of Wales, but chiefly the islands and mainland caves of Pembrokeshire. Marking of these pups has shown that there is an explosive dispersal soon after they leave the nurseries in late autumn, north in the Irish Sea, west as far as western Ireland, and south to Brittany (one to the north coast of Spain). Most of the recoveries are of adolescent seals shot by fishermen and other gunners; in effect the Welsh herd is a reservoir providing colonists to strengthen the depleted grey seal population on shores where the species is much hunted — especially Ireland and Brittany. Perhaps they are the more easily approached and killed abroad from the fact that they have become tame and accustomed to man at their Welsh nurseries, where boatmen convey visitors to within easy photographing distance of their hauling out on rocks and beaches (Plate 7).

At the time when Neale, a reliable observer, visited Grassholm eighty years ago he estimated that the puffins there at about half a million. Today there may be less than five couples. But as there are no rats or rabbits at Grassholm, it seems certain that the puffin burrowed the shallow haystack of fescue and other grasses which covered Grassholm (there is no soil to speak of on this small basaltic islet) until it became a positive ' slum ', that is, untenable when rain and weather broke down the flimsy ceilings, leaving the soft surface in its present deeply pitted condition. At about this time (1890) intensive farming of both Skomer and Skokholm ceased, and rabbits were allowed to open up the hedges and once-cultivated fields. Already by 1927 when I went to live at Skokholm there were some 20 000 pairs of puffins breeding there, where previously, during the farming era of the last century, this species had been confined to a few cliff sites; and possibly four times that number at Skomer (as contemporary photographs show). It seems reasonable to suppose that as Grassholm became unsuitable for nesting, the majority of puffins moved to Skomer and Skokholm in one or two decades around 1900.

In the last quarter century, however, there has been another considerable change in sea-bird numbers: puffins on Skomer and Skokholm have suffered a ten-fold decrease. All those burrows which they occupied as they were opened up by rabbits in the old farm fields and hedge-walls have now been deserted by puffins, and most of them taken over by the large increasing population of Manx shearwaters. The puffins are confined to cliffs and cliff slopes. In the same period there has been an alarming decline in the numbers of cliff-nesting guillemots and razorbills. This general decrease of the three auks has been recorded throughout the Welsh colonies, as well as at those of southern English cliffs; so that it is evidently due to some external adverse factor. At present oil pollution at sea is generally blamed; since the auks live largely by swimming and diving they are more prone to be caught in slicks of tarry residue discharged by tankers than the free-flying gulls and petrel species.

On the credit side is the increase in shearwaters, fulmar and storm petrels breeding in Wales. Protection at their nesting islands may account for some, but perhaps not all, of this increase — it is hard to be sure. For the gulls have also increased in the same period — a change looked on with less approval by conservationists, who are inclined to blame some of the decrease of the auks on the activities of the three *Larus* species, the greater and lesser black-backed and herring gulls. The success of the gulls has almost certainly been due to the availability of new sources of food provided by man in the form of edible wastes dumped at rubbish tips, sewage farms, town parks and fishwharves; and at sea unsaleable fish and fish offal thrown overboard in large quantities day and night after each clearance of trawl and net by numerous fishing vessels. Unfortunately the *Larus* gulls find it more convenient during the nesting season to hunt and feed close at home. Greater black-backed gulls take adult, eggs and chicks of the three auks, as well as the eggs and chicks of kittiwake gulls. Herring gulls are great egg and young chick killers, and also rob the adult auks of fish carried in to feed their young. The lesser black-backed gull is the least offender, as well as limited to comparatively few nesting sites in Wales. The kittiwake, innocent of predation on other birds, has also shared in the general increase in numbers: it is a feeder on small pelagic organisms, but will follow fishing boats at sea to scavenge and clean up after the large gulls and fulmars have taken the bulk of the waste fish and offal.

It is often said that the predator must live in equilibrium with and not exterminate its prey; that man should not interfere with this relationship. Nevertheless, some control of greater black-backed gulls attempted at Skomer and Skokholm seems to have met with satisfactory results judged by a corresponding reduction in the number of skins of auks and shearwaters counted at the feeding sites of this gull.

Without rabbits the larger islands tend to become overgrown with bracken, bushy vegetation and low wind-blown scrub woodland, conditions which are generally unsuitable for most nesting sea-birds. Intensive grazing by cattle and sheep has shown that the small islands became rather uninteresting pasture with relatively few plant species, while the heavy tread of the ' golden hoof' breaks down the burrows of ground-nesting birds. On the whole the rabbit is regarded by the naturalist as an asset on the island reserves of Wales. Its light weight and burrowing help to maintain the underground passages used by nesting puffins, shearwaters and storm petrels. It also has a marked effect on the vegetation. Its selective feeding habits result in the production of dense showy communities of Alexanders (*Smyrnium olusatrum*), hemlock (*Conium maculatum*), bluebells and locally henbane (*Hyoscyamus niger*) in the higher parts, and vernal squill (*Scilla verna*), sea campion (*Silene maritima*), scurvy-grass (*Cochlearia* species), thrift (*Armeria maritima*) and other maritime plants nearer the cliff edge or shore. All the same, as Lacey's studies on Ynys Seiriol have shown (*Nature in Wales*, Vol. 3, No. 3, 1957), the vegetation of small islands is very easily modified by changes in the animal population.

Not the least useful of the rabbit's activities is the production on islands, as upon downs, of a short sward, dry and easy for man to walk upon.

XIII

CONSERVATION OF THE SHORES AND SHALLOW
SEAS AROUND WALES

E. I. S. REES, B.SC., *Marine Science Laboratories, Menai Bridge, Anglesey,* and P. HOPE JONES, *North Wales Naturalists' Trust.*

THE COASTLINE OF WALES and its off-shore islands approaches 1000 miles in length and is one of the country's greatest natural assets. It encompasses the full range of coastal habitats from salt marsh and estuary through sandy beaches and dunes to boulder strewn rocky shores and sea cliffs. This variety of habitat is in several places found within the space of only a few miles and the diversity of the flora and fauna within these small areas makes them valuable for field studies in marine biology. There has been a long tradition of marine natural history in Wales and not a few species were first described from Welsh localities. During the Victorian period there was a great upsurge of interest in marine biology along with most other branches of natural history. Many of the great Victorian naturalists visited the Welsh seaside resorts: Charles Darwin visited Barmouth in the summers of 1828 and 1829, while P. H. Gosse, one of the most prolific writers of the era, worked extensively at Tenby. In the north a vigorous group from the Liverpool Biological Society, led by Professor W. A. Herdman, collected widely during the 1880s and 1890s. For several years a marine biological station was operated in the old signal station on Puffin Island (Ynys Seiriol) off the easternmost corner of Anglesey. The problem of access and the loss of several boats induced them to move to Port Erin in the Isle of Man, where the station still operates as part of Liverpool University.

During the period from 1900 to 1945, when field biology was less fashionable in the schools and colleges, there was less activity on the shore. However, there was a strong bias towards marine biology in the zoology department at Aberystwyth in the years between the two wars, and a list of the marine fauna of the district was included in a special volume prepared for the British Association meeting in 1922. By the mid 1930s natural history, having changed its name to ecology, was becoming academically respectable again and zoology students were once again encouraged to look at live animals in their natural surroundings. An annual field course in marine biology has been run at Bangor every year since 1935. The upsurge in ecology was felt most in the years immediately after the last war. The two most significant events in Wales were the opening of Dale Fort Field Centre in Pembrokeshire in 1947 and the founding of the University of Wales marine biological station (now the Marine Science Laboratories of the University College of North Wales) on the shores of the Menai Straits. Since then the demand for facilities to study marine biology in the field has far outstripped what these two centres can provide and during the Easter spring tide periods, parties from schools, training colleges and universities from all over Britain, can be found billeted in a variety of accommodation near the favoured localities. There are now flourishing research schools in marine biology at Bangor and Swansea, while the geology department at Aberystwyth has a strong interest in marine palaeo-ecology. Research workers from Leeds, Manchester, Liverpool, Birmingham and Bristol universities also find that the Welsh coast is often the most convenient area for their work. At Conway the Ministry of Agriculture, Fisheries and Food has a research laboratory devoted mainly to the development of techniques for rearing shellfish, and an oil pollution research unit is attached to the Orielton Field Studies Centre in Pembrokeshire.

Although man has had an increasingly significant effect on the terrestrial ecology of the British Isles for thousands of years, it is only in the last hundred years or so that he has had any noticeable effect on the surrounding sea. Even now the effects on the sea as a whole are slight but they sometimes make themselves felt in shallow coastal waters. The bland assumption that the sea has an infinite capacity to dilute, disperse and break down our waste products has received a timely jolt from the discovery of DDT residues in Antarctic seabirds and the high concentrations of polychlorinated biphenyls in auks recently found dead in the Irish Sea and the Baltic. While the vast majority of the domestic and industrial wastes that find their way into the sea are quickly rendered harmless or are broken down by bacteria, an increasing number of non-biodegradeable compounds are being created. Some of these materials are giving rise to considerable concern as they are apt to be concentrated by living organisms at each step along the line of a food chain until they reach toxic concentrations in the organisms at the top of the chain. The group of organo-chlorine compounds (of which DDT and PCB are members) and various heavy metal compounds are the source of most concern at present. In the sea the dispersive effects of the tides and currents may carry pollutants a long distance from the source.

Conservation in the marine environment around Britain has up to the present time usually meant the preservation of the livelihood of commercial fishermen. Since the 19th century the local Sea Fisheries committees and the Ministry of Agriculture, Fisheries and Food have been able to control activities that could be proved to be detrimental to the commercial fisheries. Unfortunately the onus has been on them to prove that harm will be done rather than for the newcomer to prove that his activity will not do any harm. In spite of this handicap the sea fisheries committees have done much that has conserved the natural history of the Welsh coast as well as the fisheries. Dr Travis Jenkins, who was for many years superintendent to the Lancashire and Western Sea Fisheries Committee, with a district extending from Barrow in Furness in the north to Newquay, Cardiganshire, in the south, was the author of the best known book on the fishes of the British Isles. Although first published in 1925 it still has not been superseded by any other reasonably-priced book.

Generally speaking the land between high and low water marks is claimed by the Crown and there is no legal right of access for the public. However, in many parts of Wales the local authorities have leased the foreshore and have given the public access for recreation. The Nature Conservancy have no exclusively intertidal nature reserves, but at a number of Welsh reserves their rights do extend to low water mark. These rights have usually been taken in order to control activities which might be detrimental to the adjoining reserve rather than to protect the shore itself. In addition, a number of sections of shore have been scheduled as Sites of Special Scientific Interest because of their value to marine biologists or as feeding areas for wildfowl and waders. A few Naturalists' Trust reserves also include sections of shore. As yet there are no sub-tidal reserves in Britain, though several countries with coral coasts have found it necessary to establish marine national parks. The time is obviously ripe for the Nature Conservancy or a similar body to be given the statutory powers to conserve representative parts of the marine environment. These powers may not be strictly necessary at the present time but they are likely to be needed in the near future and they can hardly be brought in sufficiently quickly to meet a specific threat.

So far it has been assumed by most people that the shore can take care of itself. This is broadly true because most marine animals have planktonic larvae that are widely dispersed and are able to recolonise areas away from the parent stock. By comparison with the land climax communities, marine communities develop very quickly and on many exposed shores denudation and recolonisation are normal events. A conservation problem does arise on some of the sheltered boulder shores of the Menai Straits that are intensively used by field course parties. Forty pairs of eager hands turning over rocks and exposing the organisms on the undersides to the wind and sun can quickly spoil the habitat. There is also a tendency to collect more of the less common members of the fauna than is strictly necessary. These problems arise mainly because so many parties get taken to the same well-known localities rather than because of an inherent shortage of suitable areas. There may be a case for controlling field course parties at some sites and instructions to replace stones should be high on any coastal conservation code. In some places extensive bait digging and searching for soft crabs by anglers has had a detrimental effect on the shore environment.

The immediate sublittoral environment is increasingly visited by divers and in some places there is a risk of over-collecting of large and decorative animals such as the sea urchin *(Echinus esculentus)*. In British waters this is unlikely to reach problem proportions as on the coral reefs of the Caribbean and East Africa where large quantities of the more decorative shells and staghorn corals have been taken away. Nevertheless, there may be a case for setting aside a few refuges where the full richness of the marine fauna can be seen by interested divers and where the fish are immune from spear guns. The conflict between divers and commercial lobster fishermen is one that will have to be resolved before long.

Under the terms of the recent international agreements to control the exploitation of the mineral resources of the sea bed, the shelf seas were divided up amongst the countries bordering those seas. Although not formally separated from the rest of Britain, about 5000 square miles of sea bed could now be described as Welsh. To date, sand and gravel are the only minerals being worked in the Welsh area. Dredging now takes place in the Bristol Channel and along the Constable Banks off North Wales. Relatively little is known about the effects of these activities, but recent observations by divers have shown that the suction dredgers leave pits up to twenty feet deep in the sea bed. How long these pits take to fill up and how long the benthic fauna takes to become re-established is not known. Gravel dredging is harmful to fisheries because boulders tend to be unearthed which damage trawling gear. The large amounts of mud that are brought into suspension cannot fail to have some effect on the fauna of the surrounding area. Generally speaking an increase in the mud content of the sea bed results in a decrease in the numbers of bivalve molluscs and an increase in the numbers of polychaete worms. Disposal of sewage sludge, dredgings from harbours and inert mineral wastes has much the same effect.

Geological structures similar to those that have yielded natural gas or oil in the North Sea have been located in Cardigan Bay and the north east Irish Sea. It remains to be seen whether the exploratory drilling now in progress off Blackpool will yield anything significant and whether further geological investigation will encourage exploratory drilling in Cardigan Bay. The possibility, however remote it may be, of a repetition of the Santa Barbara Channel affair will cause concern to many conservationists and local authorities. In the Santa Barbara Channel, off California, an oil well accident resulted in a seepage of oil through the sea bed which went on for several months in spite of the most sophisticated techniques that were used to try to stop it. Natural gas is not without its drawbacks either. A pipeline terminal complete with continuously flaring stack would not improve the magnificent sweeping vista of Cardigan Bay. It has been suggested that these gas flares may be as fatal for migrating birds in thick weather as are several of the Welsh lighthouses. Less tangible evidence will be found lying about in the morning however!

The population of Wales is concentrated in the industrial areas of the south east and north east, while the west coast has only relatively small settlements. As a result the volume of sewage entering the sea per mile of coast is at least ten times greater on the north and south coasts than in Cardigan Bay. In addition the water quality off the north and south coasts is probably influenced by the discharges from the Merseyside and Bristol conurbations. Domestic sewage has a two-fold effect on the sea. It increases the quantity of nutrient salts and hence the potential phytoplankton productivity but it also increases the turbidity of the water and so cuts down light penetration. The complex interaction of these two factors is improperly understood but there is evidence that it can alter the balance between the species in the phytoplankton, and that single species blooms are more prone to occur. Sometimes the species that blooms is toxic, as was the case when a bloom of *Gymnodinium* sp. caused an outbreak of paralytic shellfish poisoning in the North Sea two years ago. A bloom of *Phaeocystis* causes the sea off North Wales to take on the appearance of a brownish-green soup each year in late May and early June. As it dies down an unpleasant sludge accumulates on the tideline in many bays and abnormal amounts of froth are found floating about. In years when there is a heavy bloom it is enough of a nuisance to be reported in the Press. Although *Phaeocystis* is characteristic of nutrient-enriched sea water there is no direct evidence as yet to link it with sewage pollution. The chemical properties of sea water are such that the concentration of sewage in sea water has to reach aesthetically unacceptable levels before it becomes a direct hazard to human health. However, several shellfish beds have had to be closed to commercial fishermen because of pollution and the mussels from Conway and the Menai Straits have to be cleansed before being sold.

The control of pollution in coastal waters is in the hands of a bewildering array of different bodies and even more bodies are involved in monitoring its effects. In spite of this multiplicity of interests, or perhaps as a result of it, only the most fragmentary information is available on the volume and chemical composition of the wastes being discharged into the sea. Much of the information is treated as confidential and one frequently finds that the officers of one statutory body are not permitted to disclose details of discharges to their opposite numbers in other statutory bodies. The situation with regard to the dumping of wastes by ships outside the three-mile-limit is even more unsatisfactory. Apart from oil, radioactive wastes and chemical warfare materials, there is no restriction whatever on dumping, although the more responsible companies engaged in this trade do voluntarily consult the Ministry of Agriculture, Fisheries and Food. This trade has grown considerably in recent years as a result of the restriction of waste disposal into rivers and inshore waters, and there is now an urgent need for legislation to control it. Waste disposal is only one of several uses that the sea is put to and as a public resource it must be seen to be managed wisely. The basis for any plan to manage a resource must be a system for gathering statistics about the use of that resource. In the same way that fishery statistics are the foundation for the calculation of the maximum sustainable yield of a fishery, so waste disposal statistics must be the basis for any pollution assessment. At the moment the disposal contractors and even some factory managers are unaware of the precise chemical nature of the material they are dumping.

We are all too familiar with the effects of oil pollution on sea birds. Unfortunately it seems almost inevitable that wherever oil is handled in any quantity some of it gets spilled. In spite of very sophisticated control systems at the new oil terminals in Milford Haven spills still seem to occur frequently. Most of these spills are small and involve less than 100 gallons of oil but larger spills involving several tons of oil occur each year. The oil pollution research unit at Orielton was set up to study the effects of repeated spills, together with the associated clean-up operations using detergents, on the shore life of the Haven. Restrictions on tank washing in coastal waters and the introduction of the 'load-on-top' system has considerably alleviated the chronic pollution of coastal waters, but the volume of oil being carried has now increased to such an extent that, although the proportion of the oil cargoes that gets into the sea is much smaller, the actual amount does not seem to have decreased greatly. Spectacular accidents happen to tankers somewhere in the world several times a year. It is only a matter of time before one of these accidents happens on one of the tanker routes off the Welsh coast. The 'Hamilton Trader' incident off the North Wales coast in May 1969, when 700 tons of heavy fuel oil was spilled, served to show up the many inadequacies in the oil pollution control arrangements set up by the government after the 'Torrey Canyon' accident in March 1967. Although, through a chance combination of winds, none of the 'Hamilton Trader' oil came ashore in North Wales it did kill at least 5000 seabirds and polluted a considerable stretch of the Cumberland coast.

Most of the dispersal agents that are now available to deal with oil at sea or on the shore are even more harmful to the marine fauna than the oil. For this reason it is desirable to treat oil slicks as far out to sea as possible and as quickly as possible. Unfortunately there still seems to be no proper organization for getting out to sea to deal with the oil slicks before they come ashore. Ashore the local authorities have drawn up schemes to combat beach pollution which include arrangements for consultation with the Nature Conservancy and the Fishery Officers to guard against the over enthusiastic use of detergents in biologically sensitive areas.

In addition to oil pollution there are several other ways in which human influence is having an effect on seabird populations. Those species which used to be taken for food and those which have adapted their habits to feed on refuse have tended to increase, while those that are particularly susceptible to disturbance and oil pollution have tended to decrease. The history of the conservation of seabird colonies in Wales is largely the history of the conservation of the offshore islands and is dealt with in Section XII of this volume. On the mainland cliffs few positive steps have been taken towards their conservation. On some cliffs increasing disturbance is being caused by rock climbers. As difficult climbs may take hours to complete the birds are kept off their eggs for long periods and later in the season the young may be chased off the ledges prematurely. It has been suggested that if the climbers kept off the main seabird cliffs for the three months from 20th April to 20th July the trouble could be avoided without any undue restriction on their sport.

Quarrying creates new sites for seabirds in some places but it has also removed other sites. The auks prefer to nest on cliffs that are directly above the sea so that their chicks can flutter down into the sea when they fledge (Plate 6). At Penmon, Anglesey, the greater part of a traditional auk colony has been quarried away. The colony was small so the damage is not serious, but a serious threat would arise if the Carreg-y-llam quarries near Llithfaen, Caernarvonshire, were ever to reopen. The adjacent cliff has the largest auk colony in North Wales, with about a third of all the guillemots breeding in this area.

Terns and other shore nesting birds such as ringed plover are particularly liable to disturbance. The little tern (Plate 6) is now reduced to a few pairs at about six sites in Wales. If it is to survive as a breeding species here for more than a few years it will have to be actively protected. As it nests on the open beach this is not an easy task but in 1969 the only successful colony in Wales was one which local naturalists surrounded by a simple fence and wardened for a good proportion of the season.

Apart from occasional conflicts with estuary fishermen, the grey seals around the Welsh coast are sufficiently numerous to give pleasure to many visitors without arousing a clamour for the control of their numbers, as happened around the Farne Islands. The Welsh colonies are small and scattered, and to avoid disturbance the pups are usually born on the storm beaches of inaccessible coves and sea caves. However, in these sites the pups are extremely vulnerable to a combination of equinoctial spring tides and rough seas. Restriction to these hazardous sites may be holding back their numbers, unlike the Farne Islands colony where the cessation of human predation resulted in a big increase in their numbers. Together with the porpoises and bottle-nosed dolphins that are regularly seen off the Welsh coast, the seals are at the top of food chains and run the risk of building up high levels of the accumulative poisons.

For many centuries the coasts of Wales and their adjacent seas have proved an incalculably valuable natural resource for the human populations of the region: as a means of transport and communication when, in early times, the lowland areas were swamps and thick woodland; as a continuous source of food throughout human history; and in recent years as a source of inspiration and recreation to visitors, and hence of income to many residents. The increasing pressure of human population, with its mobility and affluence, is in danger of damaging the coast beyond repair, and the seas to an unknown degree, unless it is realized that these resources are not limitless in the amount of pressure and pollution that they can absorb. The concept of multi-purpose land use can be applied in many coastal areas; for example, the demands of increasing numbers of those seeking recreation can often be channelled in ways which are not inimical to the native wildlife. In other situations where there is little room for compromise, the losses of some plants and animals could be mitigated by the establishment of refuges where the continued existence of the wildlife had a high priority. At national and international level though, there are very difficult problems of resource use and of environmental pollution, and these can be tackled effectively only by governments; it is to be hoped that short-sighted economic and political expediency will not win the day over that considered, planned, careful use which the Welsh coast deserves and which it would amply repay in value to our own and future generations.

XIV

THE POLECAT IN WALES

K. C. WALTON, M.SC.

West Wales Naturalists' Trust

IT SEEMS FITTING that this book should contain an article on polecats since, as will become apparent, they are particularly associated with Wales. Their name, supposedly derived from the French ' poule-chat' (chicken-cat), is slightly misleading since they are members of the weasel family. In most parts of Britain the dark form of the domestic ferret is called by the name ' polecat' whereas in Wales the name is used for either the wild or domestic animal. The two forms are, of course, closely related. Most people regard them as the same species and it is certain that whatever differences exist between them are due entirely to selective breeding of ferrets over many centuries. No one knows where or when the ferret was first domesticated and used for bolting rabbits but there is an account of them in action in the Balearic Islands in Roman times. Nor is it known from which of the two wild polecat species of the Old World the ferret originated, or whether both were involved. These two species are the European polecat *(Putorius putorius)* found throughout Europe and into European Russia, and the Asiatic polecat *(Putorius eversmanni)* which occurs mainly in Asia as far east as the Amur River. The ranges of these two species overlap in eastern Europe but they apparently remain separated by differences in habitat preference, so that hybrids are rare.

The polecat found in Britain is the European polecat and it is one of our native mammals. It was once common and widespread in Britain but it has always been regarded as ' vermin ', sharing with the stoat and weasel the reputation of a wanton killer of domestic poultry. Its name is often mentioned amongst estate records and it also appears on churchwardens' accounts since at one time a bounty was paid for each one killed. In addition it was trapped for its fur and sometimes hunted with hounds. Despite these various pressures it continued to maintain itself until the middle of the nineteenth century when numbers began to decline and the area occupied by the animal was greatly reduced. By the early years of the present century it occurred only locally. The last animals in Scotland had been trapped by 1907;

PLATE 7. A yearling grey seal and young seal markers on one of the Pembrokeshire islands. Marking of pups such as this has shown that there is a dispersal
as far as western Ireland, Brittany and the north coast of Spain.

PLATE 8

The p o l e c a t in its summer coat; the face patches a r e separate and the coat is thin.

The elusive otter; at present a scarce animal in Welsh rivers.

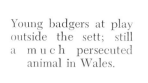

Young badgers at play outside the sett; still a m u c h persecuted animal in Wales.

a few survived in parts of England until the nineteen thirties. The only part of Britain where polecats continued to flourish was in Central Wales and just over the border and even here they suffered from the widespread use of gin-traps in areas where rabbits were trapped commercially.

In 1965 I began an investigation of the polecat which continued until 1967. The following account is based mainly on this work.

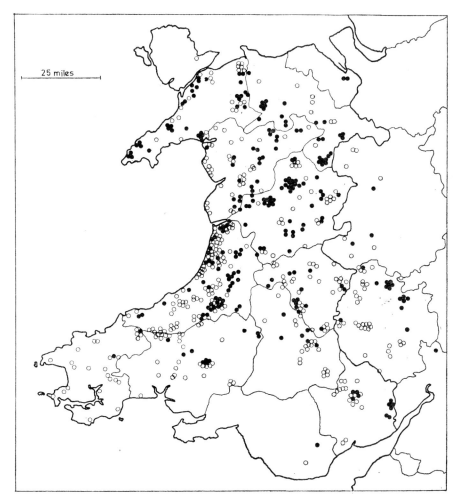

FIGURE 2. Distribution of the polecat in Great Britain, 1959-69. Each symbol represents one animal, as far as possible. ● 1959-63   O 1964-69

I started collecting records of polecats in 1959 although some of the records are older than this. Whenever possible I tried to get an exact date and location for each record, and as many animals as possible were examined to confirm their identity. The collection of records continues and so far they have provided the basis for a distribution map, the first time that one has been available in Britain. The information is shown in Fig. 2. with the earlier records summarised up to 1963 and recent additions shown separately. Records also continue to be received from the original area. It can be seen that there has been a considerable change in the area occupied during the ten years for which records are available.

It is reasonable to suppose that many of the records simply reflect increased and more systematic collection of data. This is certainly true for those pockets inside the main area of distribution which have been filled only recently. There is much circumstantial evidence to show that this is not so for the areas around the margin of the earlier distribution. For example, the spread into south-west Wales is quite recent. I have spoken with people who have lived in this area for most of their lives and polecats were practically unknown there ten years ago. This also seems to be true for south and south-east Wales, parts of Denbighshire and the extreme northern part of the animal's range in Caernarvonshire. In addition, whilst polecats have apparently always been present in the nearby English counties, they have recently become increasingly common in Herefordshire and Shropshire. Although Gloucestershire still has only one recent record, there was one definite record and several unconfirmed reports from Worcestershire in 1968. One of the most remarkable recent records is from Anglesey where polecats have been absent since almost the beginning of the present century. Further information from this county would be very welcome, as would additional records from the other end of the country, where polecats seem to be flourishing in the wet coastal area between Cardiff and Newport.

Many of the records have come from river valleys, which is hardly surprising since polecats are often killed by traffic, and roads in Wales tend to follow the valleys. There is, however, another possible explanation. In a country as mountainous as Wales there is an abundance of prey along the lower ground, which must become increasingly scarce higher up. Some continental authors have commented on the polecat's preference for waterways and put this down to its liking for frogs, which certainly form an important part of its diet.

PHYSICAL FEATURES

In shape the polecat resembles the stoat, with a long sinuous body and short legs. Male polecats measure, on average, 52 cm. from nose tip to tail tip; whilst females measure slightly less, 46 cm. The average weight of males, 987g. is, however, considerably greater than that of females at 623g.

Young polecats have a thin covering of white hair when first born, which is replaced when they are about twenty days old with a dark coat. By the age of fifty days the young have a typical polecat appearance with the characteristic white facial markings.

The coat of the polecat after this age consists of two types of hair — the under-fur or wool, and the contour or guard-hairs. The proportion of these types varies between the juvenile and summer coats on the one hand and the adult winter coat on the other. In both the former the density of wool and guard-hairs is reduced. The wool is buff over most of the body but greyish over the shoulders and fore limbs, rump and hind-limbs, and on the tail. This makes the extremities appear very dark. In addition, the guard-hairs are pigmented dark brown almost to the base which gives the animal a very dark appearance.

In the winter coat the wool is much longer and denser and whiter except over the extremities where it remains greyish. The guard-hairs are much longer and the basal half of each is white; also the denseness of the wool forces the guard-hairs to stand out at a greater angle from the body. The combined effect of these differences is to make the winter coat appear much lighter than either the summer or the juvenile coat.

The white face markings are very distinct features of the polecat. All polecats have white ear tips, a white chin patch extending onto the muzzle, and white cheek patches. In the juvenile and summer coats these are the only white facial markings (Plate 8). In winter there are varying degrees of development of the white frontal band which appears across the forehead to unite the cheek patches. Occasionally the latter also develop downwards to join the chin patch, giving the animal a complete white band around the face.

The only variation in the coat pattern from that described above is that a few animals show slight extensions of the chin patch onto the throat, usually associated with a scattering of white hairs on the limbs. This condition may be due to recent crossing with escaped ferrets. From time to time animals are found in which the black pigment is replaced by a reddish one — the so-called 'red' polecats. About twenty to thirty years ago these were found occasionally from mid-Cardiganshire to Merionethshire. There are few recent records, however, and I have seen only one such animal during ten years, from Llandinam in Montgomeryshire.

AGE ESTIMATION

In a study of any animal we need to know something about the ages of the individuals concerned to enable us to understand such features as breeding, growth, and expectation of life. Many methods of age estimation have been used but most of them become less reliable with increasing age of the animal and are more useful in the first months or years of life.

In the polecat the time when the band of cartilage (epiphysis) on the long bones closes is useful for a limited period of the year. This is also true for the time of closure of the skull sutures. These indicators cease to be useful earlier in the female than in the male.

The male possesses one indicator which the female lacks — the baculum, or os penis. This bone is small and lightly-built in the juvenile male and its weight can be used to distinguish juvenile males from adults during the period July to December. At the end of this time the baculum weighs about 300 mg and the distinction ceases to exist. No satisfactory method has been found of separating animals into groups from different years.

From the proportion of juvenile to adult males in the population during the period after the breeding season, it is possible to calculate the life expectancy of males at birth as being slightly over eight months.

BREEDING

Most of the animals examined were males, almost four times as many as females. Many of the females were juvenile so that they added little to our knowledge of reproduction. This uneven sex-ratio is itself interesting since a similar situation has been observed in several of the weasel family; in the pine-marten amongst the oldest part of the population, and in the weasel when populations are low. If we assume that equal numbers of both sexes are born, and there is some suggestion in published work that this is not necessarily the case, what could possibly account for the ratio actually found in the polecat? There is some evidence from stoats and weasels which suggests that males wander more widely over larger areas than females and are thus more likely to be trapped or killed by traffic. Any count based on animals from these sources therefore would be biased. This seems to be the most probable answer, but it is also possible that males survive better than females as juveniles. There is a marked difference in the rate of development between the sexes with the male always ahead in terms of size and body weight. The result of this is most apparent when the animals reach maturity, and it can be imagined that, even as juveniles, the males would tend to get more than their fair share in times of food shortage!

It seems likely that only one litter a year is born, in about June. The evidence for this is circumstantial since few observations have been made on females during the breeding season. The marked shortage of females during the months from February to June suggests that they become secretive and move about only slightly during this period. However, there is no evidence of two different generations of young during the latter part of the year, as there would be if two litters were normally produced. Also, the few adult females found in July and August were not pregnant, but had already given birth to young that year.

The most likely month for birth was calculated from the earliest that young animals have been found out of the nest. This was 20th July and the tooth development of these young was comparable to that of young ferrets known to be sixty days old. This places the date of birth around the end of May, and most young animals were found in August so that they would have been born in June.

The gestation period is forty-two days so that mating, by this method of reckoning, must occur in April. This fits in well with the direct observations which I have made on reproduction in the male. The testes begin to develop in December. Their weight rises steeply from January to March and remains at a peak from then until May, when it falls rapidly. Spermatozoa are most abundant during only the peak period and are very scarce in June. This is an additional reason for supposing that there is no second litter. Both sexes are mature in the Spring of the year following their birth.

ANNUAL CHANGES IN NUMBER: CAUSES OF DEATH

The frequency of polecat records for each month of the year is shown in Fig. 3. It can be seen that most of the animals (52%) were recorded during the period August to November. This is the period when young animals appear in the population and suffer a heavy mortality. For animals of all age groups, in which the cause of death was known, 86% had been killed by traffic or traps. The remaining 14% had been killed by shooting, dogs or snares; or had been found dead. Two animals were examined which showed signs of poisoning by an anti-coagulant poison, such as one of those used for rodent control. Several other records, for which animals were not examined, suggest that this is a fairly common occurrence. What usually happens is that a farm is treated with one of these poisons during the winter to control rats, and one or more dead polecats are found amongst the hay as this is used up. Rats which have been poisoned with anti-coagulants are lethargic for some time before death and more easily caught by predators such as the polecat. There must be many other causes of mortality in addition to those for which man is responsible.

Broken teeth are commonly found. Abscesses on the teeth and jaw, and around the head and neck are found more rarely.

THE FOOD OF THE POLECAT

It is possible to build up a picture of an animal's diet by a variety of means. Direct observation, which has provided such useful information for birds, is almost valueless for the polecat which is largely nocturnal, although one or two most useful pieces of information have emerged this way. I have had to rely mainly on the examination of stomach contents of dead animals, which gives a guide to the main items of diet. Prey species which have been identified are as follows: —

(a) *Mammals* — rabbit (or hare), water-vole, short-tailed vole, wood-mouse, hedgehog.
(b) *Birds*
(c) *Amphibians and reptiles* — common frog, common lizard.
(d) *Invertebrates* — These include moth and fly larvae, earthworms, adult beetles, a harvestman and a bumble-bee.

Many stomachs contain plant material but the type and quantity (grass, leaves) indicate that these are taken incidentally with animal prey. In addition to this list, polecats have been seen hunting and eating rats by day, and feeding at night from a hare carcass which had been killed by a car. In terms of quantity, small mammals and frogs seem to be most important items of diet.

This list is certainly not comprehensive, but still shows that the polecat eats a wide variety of prey. The animals eaten reflect the polecat's method of hunting, which depends largely on its sense of smell. When rabbits and voles are taken, for example, these are often young animals from the nest.

PARASITES OF THE POLECAT

The external parasites most commonly found on polecats are ticks of the species *Ixodes hexagonus*. About a quarter of the animals examined have these ticks, which are present in various stages of their life-cycle. The numbers found are usually few. Occasionally there are large numbers of the immature forms (up to sixty-five nymphs on one occasion) and as many as a dozen adults have been recorded from one polecat. The dog-tick *(Ixodes canisuga)* has been found twice.

Fleas are found only rarely and the species appear to be those easily acquired from prey animals.

Internal parasites were found in a few individuals and included a tapeworm *(Taenia tenuicollis)* and a nematode *(Molineus patens)*, both widespread amongst members of the weasel family as parasites of the stomach and intestine. Another nematode *(Skrjabingylus nasicola)* often infects the nasal cavity of the polecat and related species, causing erosion of the skull between and above the eyes.

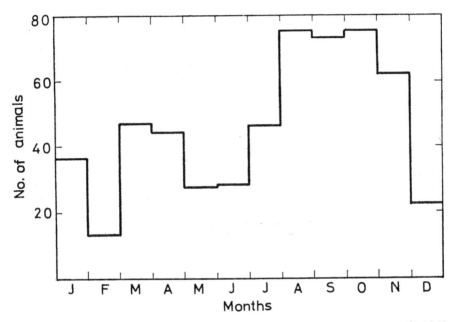

FIGURE 3. Number of polecats recorded for each month of the year, 1959-1969 inclusive.

There is little doubt that at the present time we are witnessing a most welcome recovery of polecat numbers. It must be assumed that this recovery is due to a change of some sort which has produced an increase in the birth rate, a decrease in the death rate, or both. One of the factors most likely to have produced such a change is the decrease in the number of gin-traps in use which must have had a considerable affect on the death rate. Before the first epizootic of myxomatosis in Britain in 1954, tens of thousands of these traps were used by professional trappers to supply rabbits for the market. Pembrokeshire, Carmarthenshire and south Cardiganshire were amongst the most important areas in Britain for this trade. It was common practice when dealing with any particular area to begin by trapping out all the local ground predators, especially stoats, weasels, foxes and polecats. This was done to prevent damage to trapped rabbits which would have reduced their market value. The procedure was so effective that stoats and weasels were considered to be locally extinct in west Wales as recently as 1952.

The first wave of myxomatosis so reduced rabbit numbers in Britain that commercial trapping was no longer economical. It was this factor and not the subsequent legislation in 1958 which reduced the number of gin-traps being used, but the legal ban should make it impossible for such a situation ever to arise again. As a result of the disappearance of wholesale trapping stoats and weasels have been re-establishing themselves in west Wales during the last ten years and polecats are common once more. The wild-cat seems to be making a similar recovery in Scotland. It seems likely that the polecat will continue to extend its range in the future, certainly into the remaining unoccupied parts of Pembrokeshire and Carmarthenshire. Some expansion can also be expected into the less industrialized parts of South Wales, and into those parts of England bordering the eastern counties of Wales.

Unfortunately the polecat is a very easy animal to trap. During trapping operations against mink in south west Wales from 1962 to 1969 a great many polecats were caught accidentally. Luckily, the majority of the trapping was carried out with cage traps so that it was possible to release polecats unharmed. Twenty were caught and subsequently released during the late summer of 1969 in the Teifi valley, an area from which polecats were absent some ten to fifteen years ago.

The gin-trap can be blamed in part for the extermination of the polecat in most of England. It was almost certainly responsible for the disappearance of the animal in Scotland where it was trapped for its fur during the nineteenth century. Records from the Dumfries Fur Market from 1830 to 1875 show that the number of skins on sale fell during this period and their price rose as they became scarcer. By 1870 there were no skins on sale and polecats were practically extinct in Scotland.

Few polecats are now trapped in Britain for their fur but both species are trapped extensively in Europe and Asia to supply the London auctions where the pelts are known by the name of 'fitch'. Figures supplied to me by a London firm of hide-brokers show that they alone handled 120 000 pelts of the European polecat from the Soviet Union and Czechoslovakia during the period 1962 to 1967. This must be only a fraction of the total output unless numbers have been greatly reduced, since a figure of 149 000 pelts has been quoted for European Russia in the one year of 1925. There seems little fear that the polecat will ever again be subjected to this sort of pressure in Britain. Nevertheless, far too many polecats are still trapped in the interests of game preservation either by means of the humane spring traps or, more often, with the illegal gin.

In Europe *P. putorius* has a very extensive distribution which is currently increasing in area, but for a different reason from that which I have given for Britain. It has been shown that its spread into Finland from 1880 to 1930 coincided with a long term change in the climate which gave rather warmer winters with less snowfall. Snow cover and freezing weather interfere with the polecat's food supply at a critical time of the year. They do not hunt small rodents beneath the snow in the way that stoats and weasels do, and freezing temperatures cause a shortage of frogs, another important item of diet. The number of polecats caught in Finland dropped to one tenth of its previous value after the hard winters of the years from 1939 to 1942. It is unlikely that climatic factors of this sort would limit the area of distribution of the polecat in Wales where winter temperatures are rarely extreme, especially along the coastal belt. However, such an effect should not be entirely discounted during winters such as that of 1962-63. In Scotland winters are relatively severe, especially in the Highlands, and this fact may well have tipped the balance against the polecat during the last century when trapping was already causing a decline in numbers. Polecats counter the effects of hard weather to some extent during the winter by moving near or into farm buildings and outhouses. Here they find adequate shelter, and rats and mice are often abundant. This behaviour has been noted both in Wales and in continental Europe. They have even been known to take scraps put out for birds.

So far I have discussed the ways in which trapping and climate may affect the polecat. There is another most important factor which must have a considerable bearing on the survival of the animal — habitat. Wales affords the polecat and many other species of wildlife a great variety of habitats, particularly marginal land, marshes, small woodlands and wide hedgebanks, which support large numbers of the animals on which the polecat feeds. Young forestry plantations create additional cover and food and, whilst the interiors of mature forests are poor in wildlife, this is not true for the rides and the forest fringes. It seems unlikely that the present pattern of land use will be altered drastically in the near future so that the polecat is well provided for in this respect. There still remains, however, the problem of road traffic which at present causes as many deaths as trapping. This seems surprising when one remembers the low density of traffic in Wales during the Autumn when the majority of the animals are killed. Two factors may have some influence on this apparent anomaly. Firstly, records collected over many years show that certain stretches of road seem to be especially dangerous. This can be explained by supposing that some highly favoured habitat occurs on either side of such stretches and that polecats cross over them more often than elsewhere, especially at night. This seems to be true for the main road south from Aberystwyth, for the road north as it passes Borth Bog and the Dovey Estuary; and for the roads round Tregaron Bog. The second factor is that polecat mothers apparently lead their young onto roads at night, or perhaps across them. Animals thus caught in the lights of an on-coming car seem to be unaware of any danger, although single adults will occasionally take up a threatening posture in such a situation — a piece of behaviour with low survival value! In either case death results and it is interesting, if sad, to witness the destruction of what appears to be an entire litter over a period of weeks at the same spot.

Whatever effect these various factors may have individually, their combined result, at least in recent years, has been increase and expansion on the part of the polecat. Let us hope that this trend will continue.

XV

THE OTTER IN RADNORSHIRE

C. W. WALKER, M.C., M.A., M.D.

Herefordshire and Radnorshire Nature Trust

THE ANXIETY expressed in letters received in 1967 from Trust members in Radnorshire as to the scarcity of the otter in the county's rivers led the Management Committee to look into the whole question of the local status of the species. Over forty persons — riparian owners, river bailiffs, keepers, fishermen, otter hunters and riverside dwellers — were approached and their help enlisted to form an opinion on the question 'Are we losing the otter?' Their combined testimony and continued co-operation have enabled the Trust to keep abreast of the situation and to provide the basis of the present account. It may be felt that as no names of witnesses or precise dates or places are given the conclusions lose cogency. If so, this cannot be helped for much of the information was given in strict confidence through anxiety for the safety of the otters if their precise haunts were specified.

The 'Otter Report' (1958), based on research undertaken for the national Otter Committee by Marie N. Stephens, states that the number of otters improved after the First World War and that by 1939 they were comparatively common. Numbers dropped during the Second World War, but again increased in the post-war period. The Report states that in the Wye River Board area 'there are plenty of otters on the rivers. They are said to be numerous on the Lugg'. No-one would use the terms 'plenty' and 'numerous' in this connection today. There are now very few otters on the Wye between Builth and Monmouth and the same may be said of the Lugg from above Leominster to its junction with the Wye. Some of the informants noticed a steady decrease since the thirties and the evidence as a whole indicates a very distinct recent and continuing reduction in the otter population. From the evidence available numbers in the Wye would seem to have dropped to about 25% of what they were fifteen years ago and rather less drastically in the main tributaries, perhaps to 50%.

THE ELUSIVE OTTER

The whole subject is beset with difficulties. Otters are very seldom seen. They lie up by day and are active only after dark. Their presence is betrayed by their seals (footprints) in mud, spraints (droppings), remains of fish partly eaten, slides and tracks in grass or snow. Such signs are obvious only to skilled and interested observers, such as the Trust's informants. Many people living near an otter-frequented river are quite unaware of their presence or at most have been apprised of it by hearing an occasional whistling call on a winter night when mating is in the air and the pair whistle to each other as the visiting dog-otter approaches his bitch from his territory a mile or more downstream. Once or twice in a lifetime a fisherman may see an otter sunning itself on a rock in midstream, or perhaps a head may appear in the pool he is fishing, give one steady stare, then quietly submerge, not to reappear, or — rarest sight of all — a dam may be seen playing with her cubs or leading them in a game of follow-my-leader down a clay slide into the water. One fisherman related how he had once seen two small objects in the Wye which at first he took to be a pair of dabchicks (little grebe), but which on closer scrutiny turned out to be the heads of two small otters. A larger head then appeared, the mother, with a chub in her mouth. Swimming gently against the stream with a cub on either side of her, the bitch held the fish while one cub fed on the head, the other on the tail, swimming all the time. The watcher claimed that this had been one of the most remarkable sights he had ever witnessed. Most of us go through life without so much as a glimpse of an otter in the wild (Plate 8).

THE HARD WINTER, 1962-3

It was the view of a number of the witnesses that the decline in numbers had been most marked in the last five or six years. The very severe winter of 1962-63 might be considered responsible for this. The smaller tributaries were then frozen and snowed over; all the deeper and slower reaches of the Wye and Lugg were icebound. All authorities agree that in previous hard winters the otter had taken to a largely non-fish diet and had preyed on moorhens, water-voles and rabbits, especially rabbits. Owing to myxomatosis rabbits in 1963 were very scarce and it is possible that many otters, like herons and kingfishers in that winter, died as a result of inability to catch fish and through lack of alternative prey. If that winter did indeed cause a significant drop in otter population, signs of recovery might be expected within four or five years; such an improvement does not appear to have materialized.

BANK CLEARANCE

Otters prefer reaches with plenty of cover provided by trees and bushes and well-known holts have often been in hollow trunks or among the roots of trees growing at the very brink of the river. The removal of such obstacles in the course of bank clearance has on occasion destroyed a traditional holt and its tenants have perforce gone elsewhere. Although bank clearance does go on intermittently, it is impossible to regard this as a major cause of otter scarcity.

HUMAN DISTURBANCE

Many of the witnesses commented on the increasing disturbance of the quiet and privacy of riversides. Angling has increased greatly and some reaches are very heavily fished. There are far more picnic parties (and resulting litter!) and many more people habitually take riverside walks, often with their dogs. Canoeing has become popular, affecting all the middle reaches of the main river. It must be admitted that all these activities take place in the daylight, while the otter is largely a nocturnal animal. Even so, if its daytime sleep in some holt or hideout is constantly being disturbed by sounds and scents of nearby dogs or human beings an otter may find life in such frequented places insupportable. More than one observer has come to the conclusion that the otters have retreated into the smaller streams to escape from all this disturbance. They mention instances of cubs born in woods or by small ponds at some distance from a stream or river, presumably in the search for greater privacy and security than that now afforded by a river-bank holt. This would account for the present scarcity of otters in the Wye throughout most of the Herefordshire part of its course and in the Lugg — both frequented by otters until recently — but it would also mean that the numbers in the smaller tributaries should now show an increase and this is certainly not the case.

POLLUTION

River pollution has probably been a major factor in the case of many English rivers, but not to anything like the same extent in the river systems of the Welsh border counties. The Wye is cleaner than it was twenty-five years ago and neither factory waste, sewage nor detergents appear to have adversely affected the fish or other forms of river life during the period under review. Agricultural and horticultural pesticides have of course come under suspicion in this, as in other cases of reduction of wild life. The insect life of rivers has demonstrably suffered in recent years. The rise of may-fly on the Dore, for example, used to be a remarkable sight on a June evening when thousands of these insects could be seen swinging up and down in their nuptial flight over the water. They are now so rare that the Dore trout can hardly be tempted by artificial may-fly, never having learnt to relish the real insect! Affected insects are taken by the fish, which, affected in their turn, form the otter's diet. A number of the informants believe that very little breeding is taking place among the remaining otters and this is ascribed by them to the action of pesticides, which are known to have had this effect in the case of certain birds of prey. In 1969, however, otters have bred in at least two Radnorshire streams and kits have been seen.

OTTER-HUNTING

Some of the witnesses are convinced that otter-hunting is the main cause of the steady decrease and it is necessary to look into this possibility. On consideration, however, it is impossible to blame otter-hunting for the dramatic drop in numbers that has taken place in the Wye itself. A slow decrease had gone on there for perhaps ten years, but the great acceleration of the process — and there is abundant testimony on this point — has occurred in the last five or six years, during which time hounds have killed hardly any otters at all on the main river. Where hunting took its toll in the past was in the shallower streams, where, when the otter was in normal numbers, they might kill three or even six otters in a day. In those days bitches were hunted without discrimination and in one small tributary where hounds one day killed two bitches, otters have not been seen since. At one well-known holt a bitch with half-grown cubs was hunted and killed and the hunt drew the same place two months later for the cubs; this holt is now untenanted. A bitch hunted in another tributary during the summer eluded the hounds but was hunted and killed a few weeks later. There is a likelihood that any bitch found by hounds may be either pregnant or have cubs at some stage short of maturity under her care; in either case her death is a disaster.

CONCLUSIONS

Various methods have been advocated to deal with the problem throughout the country. An Otter Protection Act might be passed, forbidding the killing of the otter by any means and making it illegal to trade in the skins of British otters. Alternatively, otter-hunting might be forbidden by law, temporarily or permanently; or Masters of Otterhounds might be persuaded in the interests of the otter and of their own sport, to declare a temporary cessation of hunting for one or more seasons. Such an arrangement is now actually being adopted in some areas. In Breconshire a number of riparian owners have forbidden otter-hunting on their respective properties as a temporary measure to secure the same result, a course of action strongly advocated by their county Naturalists' Trust.

A number of the witnesses are convinced that legislation against otter-hunting alone would result in a recrudescence of the old practices of trapping and shooting otters and would thus defeat its own object. In the absence of hunting it is claimed that many more otters would be killed. If this is true, there is a case for allowing hunting to continue should the otter again become plentiful. Other arguments in support of hunting appear to be out-of-date and no longer valid. No one, farmers and those with fishing interests included, now regards otters as vermin, or considers that the hunts are performing a public service in controlling their numbers. On the contrary, the otter is regarded by everyone as a harmless, interesting and intelligent animal whose loss as a member of the local fauna would be a matter for profound regret. Such an outcome would of course mean the end of otter-hunting and the threat of it has led the Masters of Otter Hounds to co-operate in the implementation of the recommendations contained in the Mammal Society's Report issued in 1969 as a result of the findings of the national survey enquiry under the chairmanship of Professor Hewer. For otter survey purposes his committee divided the country into fourteen areas, including the Wye river system in their Severn (No. 10) area in which, taken as a whole, the status of the otter was regarded as 'stationary'. This does not imply a satisfactory state of affairs in the Wye and its feeders and the activities of the Hawkstone Hunt have in consequence been drastically reduced. The Master has reported that hounds have found more frequently in 1969 than in preceeding seasons and that meets have taken place and hounds have been employed only to ascertain the presence, or otherwise, of otters. Care has been taken by him to ensure that no ' kill ' should take place. Whether this armistice will enable the species to recover its former numbers remains to be seen. Some breeding is taking place in the smaller tributaries. Should saturation be achieved there, young otters in search of unoccupied territory should tend to re-occupy the vacant reaches in the larger tributaries and in the Wye itself, provided that no continuing adverse factor occurs to inhibit such a return movement. Certainty on this head will only be reached after several more years have elapsed. In the meantime the situation must be kept under continual review, in order to pinpoint and, if possible, eliminate the root-causes of the otter's present scarcity.

XVI

A REVIEW OF BUTTERFLIES IN NORTH WALES

H. N. MICHAELIS

North Wales Naturalists' Trust

'THE EXTINCTION of British Butterflies is by no means so improbable a contingency as some might be disposed to imagine.' This quotation is not taken from newspapers or 'Letters to the Editor' of recent years. It is from an article in the Entomologist's Annual of 1858 by H. T. Stainton, one of Britain's leading lepidopterists. Similar views have been expressed regularly since, yet as any naturalist will have observed in 1968-69, butterflies are still numerous (Plate 9). There is a decline in numbers, especially in areas of dense population, caused by the increasing use of land for housing and industry. Conversely, there is evidence of a few species extending their range over the past thirty years.

Until the late S. Gordon Smith produced his volumes on the Butterflies and Moths of Cheshire and North Wales from 1948-54, only three local lists dated 1884, 1903 and 1910 were known. These, together with scattered notes in entomological journals, were the source from which an idea of distribution could be formed and most of this information related to the vicinity of holiday resorts. The writer has had some local experience from 1917 to 1930 and again since 1964, with intermittent visits between those periods. From these sources an attempt is made to indicate the distribution of butterflies from Anglesey, Caernarvonshire, Denbighshire, Flintshire, Merionethshire and Montgomeryshire. Distribution is shown on general lines rather than in detail and there is much scope for future observation. It should be realised that part of the distribution of North Wales butterflies discussed here, especially of the southern area, is not based always on up-to-date records and any recent information would be appreciated.

Before dealing with species, the probable causes of the decline in numbers are examined under several headings. In the text 'larva' is used to indicate the caterpillar, 'pupa' is used to denote the chrysalis or dormant stage and 'imago' is used for the butterfly. 'Univoltine' or 'bivoltine' mean single-brooded or double-brooded respectively. The terms 'food' or 'foodplant' refer to that of the larva except where it is stated to refer to the imago.

PLATE 9. Four butterflies still widespread in Wales. *Above left*, speckled wood; *right*, red admiral; *below left*, small copper; *right*, peacock; all photographed at Treborth, near Bangor, Caernarvonshire.

CAUSES OF DECLINE

1. *Climate.* A series of poor summers from 1960 to 1967 had an adverse effect on numbers. A slight recovery in some species was noticed in 1967 and this continued in 1968 and 1969.

2. *Development in housing and industry.* This occurred mainly in the region of established populated areas and foodplants of many species were destroyed, for only the ' Whites ' will feed on a few garden plants and vegetables. Grass and nettles on undeveloped land and waste ground so often found near industrial buildings may both provide temporary feeding grounds. Flowers of buddleia, lavender, valerian, michaelmas daisy and other garden flowers provide the food for the imagines essential for reproduction and even then, the food on which the female will lay eggs may not be easily available. Consequently, butterflies are scarcer in urban or suburban areas than on undeveloped land.

3. *Insecticides and herbicides.* These may be considered together as the first destroys insects and the second may destroy their food. Much has been written on the use and misuse of insecticides and it is clear that spraying over a wide area will kill many insects. There is no discrimination and both pests and their predators and parasites are destroyed. It is not always realised that insecticides and weedsprays can produce deleterious effect on the reproductive ability of fauna generally. Sprays used to control vegetation may be general or selective and however carefully applied, may be carried by wind on to herbage other than that to be controlled. There is little evidence of the use of insecticides or herbicides on a large scale in North Wales. Local authorities appear to rely on the cutting of roadside verges rather than on the destruction of vegetation by spraying, though it is observed that certain ' hard ' weeds such as dock, nettle, ragwort and buttercup are controlled by this means.

4. *Cutting of roadside verges and banks.* High growth and overhanging vegetation is controlled in the interests of safety but is the almost lawn-like mechanical shaving of sloping banks as practised by some County Councils so necessary? In addition to foodplants, the early stages of many butterflies feeding on the roadside flora are destroyed. It is likely that fumes and deposit from petrol and diesel vehicles have an adverse effect and the regular parking of vehicles on verges certainly contributes to the destruction of the flora and fauna. Comparison with forty or fifty years ago, shows a noticeable reduction in numbers of butterflies seen or found breeding on well-used country roads.

5. *Afforestation with conifers*. The greater part of land planted by the Forestry Commission in North Wales is high moorland of grass, heather and associated plants. There has also been a considerable replacement of deciduous woodland at lower levels with conifers by the Commission and private owners; the main trees affected are oak, ash, birch, elm and beech. In the early stages of growth, a conifer plantation will support the existing herb layer to some extent but as the conifers mature, this undergrowth will disappear. As no British butterfly feeds on conifers, the change in the herb layer affects mainly the four woodland species of fritillary found in North Wales as all feed on species of violet. These species still occur though numbers are much reduced when compared with the 1920-30s. The draining and planting of wet moss and moorland has reduced and destroyed some colonies of the large heath butterfly which feeds mainly on the white beaked-sedge *(Rhynchospora alba)*. Conversely, the speckled wood has maintained its status in grass rides and forest road edges; the green hairstreak has increased where bilberry is established, for the grazing of bilberry by sheep had reduced the numbers in upland areas. It is possible that the practice of edging conifer plantations with hardwoods may assist the regeneration of the herb layer and, in time, the status of woodland butterflies.

6. *The decline in the rabbit population*. Seedlings, especially of sloe and hawthorn, previously controlled by rabbits prior to the myxomatosis outbreak, have now developed into dense thickets which smother small herbaceous plants. This is noticeable on the limestone of Flintshire, Denbighshire and Caernarvonshire where sloe has increased considerably in the past decade. Gorse has also increased in many areas. Rabbits also controlled the growth of grasses which have increased on some nature reserves and ungrazed commons thereby smothering small plants. Winter grazing by cattle could be tried as a control of grass. Vetches, rockrose and some crucifers are the foodplants mainly affected.

7. *Predators and parasites*. Predators include birds, rodents, carnivorous insects and some reptiles, all of which may destroy the butterfly in any stage. Parasites are *Hymenoptera* (ichneumons, braconids and chalcid wasps), which lay their eggs in or on the eggs and larvae, and *Diptera* (two-winged flies) which deposit eggs on the butterfly eggs and larvae or on adjacent leaves. The resulting hymenopterous or dipterous larvae burrow into the body of the caterpillar and feed on the fat and tissue; when full grown, the parasitic larva will cause the death of the butterfly caterpillar or pupa. Some parasites are specific in their choice of hosts, so a reduction in a species of parasite may

result in an increase of the host species of butterfly or vice versa; this may partly explain the increase of the peacock butterfly in 1968-69. Such an increase will be temporary for parasites and predators will reduce the population eventually to the original level or perhaps for a short time below that level. Other natural controls are virus diseases and fungi which mainly attack larvae and pupae.

8. *Farming.* The important and essential sheep-rearing industry has an adverse effect on a few species in that close grazing will affect the early stages. The same may be said of the removal of hedges to provide a more economic use of modern farm machinery. Though no larva feeds on normal hedging shrubs, hedges do provide shelter for food-plants.

DISTRIBUTION

As stated previously, any account of distribution must be incomplete but a reasonable picture based on available information can be presented. Species are listed under family headings and a general account of local distribution and habitat is given. Details of life histories and other information may be found in the many books on British butterflies.

PIERIDAE

Seven species of 'Whites' and 'Yellows' occur, of which five are native and two are migrants. Four of the five native species are common, one migrant is scarce and the other occasional in appearance.

The large white *(Pieris brassicae* L.) and the small white *(P. rapae* L.)are bivoltine and are generally common below 1000 ft though the former when migrating flies over our mountain ranges. Both feed on species of the cabbage family *(Cruciferae)* and on the garden nasturtium *(Tropaeolum).* The large white is strongly reinforced each year by migrants from Europe during the summer and frequently emigrates to Europe in the autumn. The small white is similarly reinforced in a lesser degree.

The green-veined white *(P. napi* L.), also bivoltine, is common on low ground throughout, though it is seen less in gardens than the previous species. It feeds on hedge-garlic, watercress and other *Cruciferae.* It becomes scarcer at high altitudes but occurs on the Carneddau above 3000 ft.

The orange-tip *(Anthocharis cardamines* L.) is univoltine and is generally common on low damp ground though it is found up to 800 ft in sheltered situations. It feeds on cuckoo-flower *(Cardamine pratensis)* and other damp ground *Cruciferae.*

117

The brimstone *(Gonopteryx rhamni* L.) is univoltine, emerging in late summer to reappear in spring after hibernation. It is absent from Anglesey, local and scarce in Caernarvonshire and Denbighshire; the majority of records are from east Flintshire, Montgomeryshire and south Merioneth. It feeds on buckthorn *(Rhamnus catharticus)* and alder buckthorn *(Frangula alnus).*

The clouded yellow *(Colias croceus* Fourc.) is a spasmodic migrant and appears mainly in the west coastal regions of Anglesey and in east Montgomeryshire; it is uncommon in areas where passage is obstructed by mountains. It feeds on lucerne *(Medicago sativa)* and may produce a brood in the summer but is not capable of maintaining itself through a British winter.

The pale clouded yellow *(C. hyale* L.) is a migrant which only occasionally reaches North Wales and records are very few. It also feeds on lucerne but is unable to maintain itself here.

A record of the wood white *(Leptidea sinapis* L.) from a woodland nature reserve in North Wales included in an article by M. G. Morris in the *Entomologist's Gazette* 1967, vol. 18. p. 63, is incorrect for it is based on a wrong determination.

SATYRIDAE

These are often known as the 'Browns', a description which fits the eight species which occur in North Wales. All except one feed on grasses and most are common throughout. All hibernate as larvae.

The wall brown *(Parage megera* L.) is bivoltine and is generally common throughout. It has increased its range over the past forty years and is found inland more frequently than in the past. The butterfly is associated with walls, dry banks, rocks and sandhills and has been found up to 1300 ft in North Wales.

The speckled wood *(P. aegeria* L.) is multivoltine for the imago may be seen from April to October. It hibernates both as larva and pupa, the latter producing the April imagines. It is our commonest woodland butterfly and appears to be increasing in numbers.

The grayling *(Eumenis semele* L.) is univoltine and is locally common especially near the coast. The habitat is steep stony slopes, cliffs or sandhills. It occurs up to 1200 ft on the lower slopes of the Carneddau and a dwarf sub-species *thyone* which Thompson found on the Great Orme, Llandudno, emerges about two weeks earlier than the typical species.

The meadow brown *(Maniola jurtina* L.) is mainly univoltine though the occurrence of fresh specimens in the late summer suggests a partial second brood. This is our commonest low ground meadow and grassland butterfly and is found from June to September. It occurs sparingly on high ground up to 900 ft.

The gatekeeper *(Maniola tithonus* L.) is univoltine and is common near hedgerows, bushy hillsides, margins of woods and lanes where the butterfly is often seen on the flowers of bramble. Compared with the 1920's, it has increased in numbers in and around the Conway valley.

The small heath *(Coenonympha pamphilus* L.) is bivoltine on lower ground and tends to become univoltine as it approaches its altitude range of 2500 ft. It is common on sandhills, meadows and hillsides throughout.

The large heath *(C. tullia* Müll.*)* is univoltine and is found on mosses and wet moorland where the white-beak sedge grows. It is very local but is often plentiful where found and its range stretches in a wide band from the east Flintshire mosses (300 ft) westward over Berwyn (2000 ft), Arenig (1400 ft), south Snowdonia and Migneint (1000-1600 ft) to reappear near the Dovey estuary at sea level. The heights shown are the maximum altitudes at which imagines occur. It is likely that a careful search on high ground would reveal undiscovered colonies. On the low mosses the imago emerges in mid-June, while on high ground the main emergence is two to three weeks later. E. B. Ford *(Butterflies, p.* 311) considers the large heath to be one of our most ancient butterflies for it is thought to have arrived in Britain towards the end of the Third Pleistocene glaciation.

The ringlet *(Aphantopus hyperantus* L.) is univoltine and is usually found near woods, in wooded lanes and in small fields enclosed by woodland. Although it does not seem to be as common as it used to be in North Caernarvonshire, records show that it is local though common where found in Merionethshire, Denbighshire and Montgomeryshire, scarce in Flintshire and absent from Anglesey.

NYMPHALIDAE

There are three sub-families with different characteristics and habits and it is proposed to deal with these under their respective headings.

NYMPHALINAE

These are the large coloured Vanessid butterflies which come readily to flowers such as valerian, buddleia, thistle, michaelmas daisy, bramble and hemp agrimony. Of the seven species which have occurred, three are migrants and two are reinforced by migration in a small degree.

The red admiral *(Vanessa atalanta* L.) migrates from southern Europe in the spring and produces one summer generation on nettle. These are often reinforced by a further migration in the summer.

Though odd specimens do hibernate here, the species is unable to survive our winter and migrates southwards in the autumn. As numbers rely entirely on migration and the resultant offspring it may vary from common to scarce from year to year.

The painted lady *(Vanessa cardui* L.) breeds in winter along the edge of the North African desert and migrates northward in the spring. The migration reaches Britain from April to June and produces a summer generation on thistle and nettle. This cannot survive our winter in any stage and the butterflies move southward over Europe and the Mediterranean in autumn. It is found throughout though numbers vary considerably from year to year.

Camberwell beauty *(Nymphalis antiopa* L.) is a scarce migrant from Europe which cannot maintain itself in Britain. Available records show that under a dozen were seen in North Wales between 1855 and 1962.

The peacock *(Nymphalis io* L.) is a common univoltine species feeding on nettle. The imago hibernates in shelters and buildings in the autumn to reappear in the spring. It is reinforced by migrants from Europe in small numbers and is usually common. It was very plentiful in 1968-69.

The large tortoiseshell *(N. polychloros* L.) is univoltine and hibernates as an imago. The larva feeds on elm, willow and sallow. Apart from a record from Merioneth in 1945, a small isolated colony at the limit of its northern and western range exists in north Caernarvonshire. It was found prior to 1884, in 1911, 1915, 1944-46 and 1948. A butterfly was seen in this area by me on 15 August 1969.

The small tortoiseshell *(Aglais urticae* L.) is univoltine and may be reinforced by a few migrants each year. It feeds on nettle and is common throughout. Hibernation takes place in buildings or any suitable shelter.

The comma *(Polygonia c-album* L.) is univoltine, hibernates as an imago and flies again in Spring. It is a woodland insect which occasionally strays into lanes and gardens. After a period of scarcity in the early twentieth century, it is becoming increasingly widespread though never plentiful, in all counties other than Anglesey. It feeds on elm and nettle.

ARGYNNINAE

Five of the six species of fritillaries found in North Wales have light brown upperwings marked with black and have silver streaks and spots on the underside of the hindwings. All five feed on *Viola* species. All our fritillaries are univoltine, hibernate as larvae and are found in woods or on open ground, rarely coming into gardens. Over the past fifty years there has been a considerable reduction in the numbers of the *Argynnis* and *Clossiana* species; this is probably due to the disturbance and clearing of established deciduous woods.

The silver-washed fritillary *(Argynnis paphia* L.) is found in or near woods and the imago comes to flowers of bramble and hemp agrimony *(Eupatorium cannabinum)*. Records are few and it is most frequent in Montgomeryshire and south Merionethshire. The only Anglesey records are for 1902 and 1907.

The high brown fritillary *(A. cydippe* L.) is scarce and local in Caernarvonshire, Flintshire and Denbighshire and is most frequent in Merionethshire and Montgomeryshire. Unless examined carefully, it is easily confused with the more common dark green fritillary; the habitats differ for the high brown is found in or near woods while the dark green flies over grassy hillsides and sandhills.

The dark green fritillary *(A. aglaia* L.) though local is often common where found. It is less frequent in the area of the Conway Valley and in Denbighshire than it used to be but is still plentiful on the Anglesey sandhills.

The Queen of Spain fritillary *(A. lathonia* L.) was reported near Machynlleth, Montgomeryshire, in September 1969. This is a rare migrant from southern and central Europe which feeds on *Viola* species. This specimen could possibly be a progeny of a spring immigrant but any larvae which result would be unlikely to survive hibernation in this country.

The pearl-bordered fritillary *(Clossiana euphrosyne* L.) is easily confused with the next species but is larger and almost always confined to woodland. It is thinly spread throughout and is considerably reduced in numbers when compared with the 1920's. So far, there are no satisfactory records from Anglesey.

The small pearl-bordered fritillary *(C. selene* Schiff.) is mainly univoltine though a few second brood imagines occasionally occur in the autumn, as in the Conway Valley in 1959. It is widely distributed on grassy hillsides, verges of woods and sandhills and is often locally common, especially on the Anglesey sandhills.

The marsh fritillary *(Euphydryas aurinia* Rott.) feeds on scabious, usually devil's bit, and is found on damp ground and hillsides. In the early stages, the larvae live gregariously in a web spun over the plant and hibernate therein. Later the larvae leave the web and feed singly. Though very local, it is found in all six counties. Precise distribution is difficult to assess for it may occur in a small area for a few seasons and then disappear, though there is no apparent change in the habitat. Ignoring suitable intervening habitats, it may reappear a few fields away from the original location.

APATURINAE

The purple emperor *(Apatura iris* L.) is one of the largest British butterflies and the few available records during the past 100 years are listed; all except that of the late Rev. E. S. Lewis, are sight records and, as I have had peacocks reported as this species, some element of doubt must occur regarding the reports from Caernarvonshire. The records are: Caernarvonshire; Portmadoc many years ago, Betws-y-coed two seen circa 1933: Montgomeryshire; Llanidloes 1875, Llyfnant Valley 1906 by E. S. Lewis, Llannerch-y-ddol Hall and Leighton Hall 1947, Pant-y-ffridd, one unconfirmed 1962. The foodplant is sallow growing in woodland.

NEMIOBIIDAE

The Duke of Burgundy *(Hamearis lucina* L.) is possibly extinct in North Wales for no records have been received for many years. There were records in 1921 from Arthog and Dolgellau, Merionethshire, where it may survive, and from 'a lane near Gloddaeth, Llandudno' prior to 1884. I saw one on a hillside near Gloddaeth in June 1929 and one was found by G. Ellis in the same area in 1943. It is univoltine and hibernates as a pupa. It feeds on cowslip, a plant which is now uncommon in the Llandudno district.

LYCAENIDAE

This family contains hairstreaks, blues and coppers. The hairstreaks are univoltine and feed on deciduous trees and shrubs. Three hairstreaks hibernate in the egg stage and the green hairstreak hibernates as a pupa. Other species hibernate as shown below.

The brown hairstreak *(Thecla betulae* L.) feeds on blackthorn, is local and uncommon in south Merionethshire and Montgomeryshire and there are a few old records from Caernarvonshire and south Denbighshire. This species must be at the edge of its range for blackthorn is plentiful in North Wales.

The purple hairstreak *(T. quercus* L.) feeds on oak and is widespread but not common in oakwoods. It is not easy to compare past and present status as the imago usually flies round the higher branches of oak and can pass unnoticed. It has declined in numbers in the Caernarvonshire woods since the 1920's.

The white-letter hairstreak *(Strymonidia w-album* Knoch) feeds on wych-elm, is mainly found in Montgomeryshire and is local and uncommon elsewhere. It is not recorded from Anglesey.

The green hairstreak *(Callophrys rubi* L.) feeds on bilberry, gorse

122

and possibly rockrose. It occurs where bilberry is present on high ground up to 2000 ft and is also found on mosses at lower levels. Widely distributed and often common, it is increasing on roadside edges and boundaries of upland Forestry Commission plantations in the northern counties where bilberry is allowed to grow protected from sheep-grazing.

The small copper *(Lycaena phlaeas* L.) is at least bivoltine, feeds on dock and sorrel and hibernates as a larva. It is widely distributed and often common though is not as plentiful on the north coast as it used to be.

The silver-studded blue *(Plebejus argus* L.) is univoltine, normally feeds on gorse, bird's-foot trefoil and possibly other *Papilionaceae* and hibernates as an egg. It is very local being confined mainly to Caernarvonshire and Anglesey though there are old records from the Merionethshire coast. A sub-species, *caernensis* Thompson, occurs on the Great Orme and is common in some years; it differs from the typical *argus* for it is smaller, feeds on rockrose and emerges about three weeks to a month earlier.

The brown argus *(Aricia agestis* Schiff.) is bivoltine, feeds on rockrose in limestone habitats and on storks-bill *(Erodium* species) on sandhills. It is common on the northern limestone, including Anglesey, local on sandhills and there are a few records from Merionethshire and Montgomeryshire.

The common blue *(Polyommatus icarus* Rott.) is bivoltine and is our commonest blue butterfly found in many habitats, being particularly common on sandhills. It feeds on various species of *Papilionaceae* (peas, vetches, etc.) and hibernates as a larva.

The holly blue *(Celastrina argiolus* L.) is bivoltine, feeds on flowers and berries of holly and buds and flowers of ivy and hibernates as a pupa. It is local and uncommon throughout with only occasional records from Anglesey and is variable in appearance, for it is fairly common in some years and scarce in others. The second brood is usually small and the species is possibly univoltine on holly at higher altitudes.

The small blue *(Cupido minimus* Fuessl.) is univoltine, feeds on kidney vetch *(Anthyllis vulneraria)*. It is possibly extinct on the northern limestone for the last records are from Denbighshire in 1935 and from Creuddyn, Caernarvonshire, in 1944. As the foodplant is common on limestone, the butterfly may be rediscovered.

HESPERIIDAE

The skippers have a rapid darting flight and rest with their wings half raised or held flat like a moth. All our four species are univoltine, three hibernate as larvae and one as a pupa.

The grizzled skipper *(Pyrgus malvae* L.) feeds on bramble, straw-berry, barren strawberry and cinquefoil and is uncommon except in a few localities in Montgomeryshire. It hibernates as a pupa.

The dingy skipper *(Erynnis tages* L.) feeds on bird's-foot trefoil and is common throughout in suitable localities.

The small skipper *(Thymelicus sylvestris* Poda) feeds on grasses and is scarce in the northern counties and is local in Merionethshire and Montgomeryshire. Its habitat is rough fields, grassy hillsides, meadows and occasionally woodland verges.

The large skipper *(Ochlodes venata* Br. & Grey) feeds on grasses and is fairly common on grassy slopes, wood margins and the grassy parts of lowland heaths and mosses.

CONSERVATION

The causes of decline listed in sections 1-8 will show some of the problems of conservation. The greater number, if not all, concern all fauna and flora and may be taken to refer to Lepidoptera generally, not only to butterflies. Conservation may be attained by creating reserves and improving the habitat where a species is already estab-lished as opposed to attempts at introduction. Even if considered desirable, introduction is unlikely to meet with success. Excepting those which are clearly on the margin of their distribution range, species associated with deciduous woodland or wet moorland seem to be in danger of decline. To refer again to the large heath, it is present in two reserves on low lying ground but no colony over 1000 ft is protected.

Recent personal experience of conservation in the Coed Gorswen National Nature Reserve (Nature Conservancy) is of interest. A small open glade was created by clearing dense alder and hazel scrub to-gether with periodic cutting back of tree regeneration and this has been maintained. The clearing has been under observation since 1965 when the only butterflies seen were the speckled wood and an occas-ional purple hairstreak. By 1969, ten species in all were seen, of which five have moved in from adjacent open land and are probably breeding in the glade, three woodland species show some increase in numbers and two migrants were regularly seen at bramble flowers.

XVII

MARSH GENTIAN AND PALE HEATH VIOLET IN WALES

R. H. ROBERTS AND W. S. LACEY, D.SC.

North Wales Naturalists' Trust

THE MARSH GENTIAN *(Gentiana pneumonanthe)* (Plate 11) and pale heath violet *(Viola lactea)* are both usually found in acid lowland heaths. These heathlands are of little agricultural value and in the past many of them have been left undisturbed either as commons or as rough grazings. But the ever-increasing demand for land for afforestation and the ease and relative economy of effort with which poor heathland can be drained by the use of modern machinery has changed the picture radically.

Although neither species can be described as rare, they are both uncommon and of limited distribution. What is more to the point is the fact that both are known to be decreasing in extent. They have already become extinct in many localities where they were once abundant. The *Atlas of the British Flora (B.S.B.I.,* 1962) shows that both have disappeared from about 50% of the localities in which they were known before 1930 — an alarming rate of decrease and unfortunately a continuing one. In Anglesey, for example, sixty-five acres of heath near Penrhos Lligwy, long noted for the abundance of its blue marsh gentians, have been planted with conifers and several acres more in the same locality have been made into a caravan park within recent years.

In Wales the marsh gentian is now found only in Anglesey. Before the turn of the century it was known to the Bangor botanist, John E. Griffith, in one Caernarvonshire locality near Llyn Crafnant but it has not been seen there for many years now and must be presumed extinct. Repeated searches in the area have failed to discover it and, in any case, much of the likely ground has long been afforested.

The pale heath violet occurs in five of the thirteen Welsh botanical vice-counties, but in fact is actually restricted to comparatively few localities.

Although both species are found in acid environments, their ecological requirements are quite distinct. The violet is a plant of shallow, well-drained, acid soils, usually developed over a highly siliceous rock or a sandy substratum. These conditions are nicely illustrated on the heath in the Cors Goch Nature Reserve and in the drier areas of the nearby Craig Wen Nature Reserve. At both places the pale heath violet grows on the drier soils on the ridges of the base-deficient (lime-free) conglomerate or grit known to geologists as the Lligwy sand-stone. Soil pH tests carried out by one of us (R.H.R.) gave values between 5·2 and 5·6 at both localities. This violet grows best on bare ground. It cannot tolerate competition and seems to thrive on areas where human interference such as periodic burning of the heath is

FIGURE 4. The pale heath violet, an uncommon plant in Wales.

customary. Observations at Cors Goch over the last few years also suggest that the break-up of vegetation along cattle tracks provides situations favourable to its growth. It is clear that trampling by cattle is of more importance for its survival than grazing as such. The plants most constantly associated with the pale heath violet at both Cors Goch and Graig Wen are: ling, bell heather (*Erica cinerea*), gorse (*Ulex gallii*), tormentil, milkwort (*Polygala serpyllifolia*), sweet vernal grass, sheep's fescue and purple moor-grass.

In contrast the marsh gentian is a plant of damp, acid heaths formed over a base-deficient substratum, often covered by a thin layer of glacial deposits. In the Penrhos Lligwy area the glacial drift shows signs of podsol formation, the upper few inches of the clay being a mottled pale grey in colour. The pH of the thin peaty soil is about 4·7 to 4·9. The most constant associates of the marsh gentian in its Anglesey localities are: cross-leaved heath *(Erica tetralix)*, purple moor-grass, bog asphodel, ling, common sundew *(Drosera rotundi-folia)*, deer-grass *(Trichophorum cespitosum)*, many-headed woodrush *(Luzula multiflora)*, tormentil, sharp-flowered rush *(Juncus acutiflorus)* and bog moss *(Sphagnum* species).

Like the heath violet, the marsh gentian sets abundant seed regularly and young non-flowering plants have been observed on bare peat where the hooves of cattle or horses have cut the surface. Indeed, in the Craig Wen area the gentian is most abundant in a more heavily grazed and trampled heath just *outside* the Reserve itself! T. A. Warren Davis has also commented recently *(B.S.B.I. Welsh Regional Bulletin,* No. 12, January 1970) on the importance of sheep and ponies as a means of maintaining such rarities as bog orchid *(Hammarbya paludosa)* and western butterwort *(Pinguicula lusitanica)* in Bryn-berian Moor, Pembrokeshire.

These observations provide some guide as to how the Craig Wen Reserve (in which both of these interesting plants occur) should be managed. The heath at Cors Goch is already managed on lines designed to encourage both the heath violet and the numerous species of orchids: fragrant orchid *(Gymnadenia conopsea)*, lesser butterfly orchid *(Platanthera bifolia)*, green-winged orchid *(Orchis morio)*, early purple orchid *(Orchis mascula)*, green frog orchid *(Coeloglossum viride)*, and the various marsh and spotted orchids *(Dactylorhiza purpurella, D. incarnata, D. ericetorum* and *D. fuchsii)* which grow on the less acid and often base-rich areas bordering the heath. This involves grazing the heath by cattle in the winter months and carrying out rotational burning of the heath vegetation in early Spring, before flowers appear or ground-nesting birds are active.

Apart from their aesthetic appeal as beautiful and uncommon wild flowers, both of these species have a considerable phytogeographical and biological interest. In Anglesey the marsh gentian reaches its most westerly locality in the British Isles; it does not occur in Ireland or in Scotland. The pale heath violet is here near the northern limit of its European distribution; only in the west of Ireland does it occur further north. On the Continent it is almost confined to the Atlantic seaboard from Normandy through western France to the north of Spain and throughout Portugal *(Viola lactea* in *Biological Flora of the British Isles,* Moore, 1958).

Hybridization between the pale heath violet and the common violet *(V. riviniana)* seems to occur frequently. The plants at the Craig Wen Reserve show a puzzling array of forms, ranging from pure *V. lactea*

127

at one extreme to typical *V. riviniana* at the other. A plant of what appeared to be an F1 (first generation) hybrid, on the evidence of its vigorous growth and large number of flowers, was found to have mostly sterile pollen and failed to set any seed. Other plants with an apparent mixture of characters had fertile pollen and good seed-set.

Strangely, there is hardly any evidence of hybridization between these violets in Cors Goch heath, scarcely a mile to the east. The real nature of the many intermediate plants at Craig Wen remains unexplained. They provide an intriguing problem for research and deserve further study.

Detailed observations on the marsh gentian are also needed, especially in relation to the establishment of seedlings and response of the mature plants to burning. Preliminary studies have already indicated that the various populations of this gentian in Anglesey differ from one another in details such as the proportion of pale-flowered and white-flowered plants and even in the breadth of the leaves.

The North Wales Naturalists' Trust can take pride in having Nature Reserves where these fascinating plants are safe to provide both aesthetic enjoyment and scientific interest for future generations. It is certain that they will discover much more about them than is known now; mean-while the plants are held ' in trust '.

XVIII

ON THE ROCKS: QUARRYING AND CONSERVATION AT CRAIG BREIDDEN, MONTGOMERYSHIRE

C. A. SINKER, M.A.

Preston Montford Field Centre and *Shropshire Conservation Trust*

" To THE BOTANIST the Breidden is an unrivalled mine of wealth. As he scrambles up the almost precipitous face of the Black Rock, above the little over-shadowed village of Criggion, he finds his feet pillowed in a cushion of Saxifrage, or crushing an exquisite bed of the delicate emerald fronds of the Oak-fern, contrasting in their tender transparent greenness with the grey, lichened, mossy, rugged stones and rocks among which their straggling roots are so firmly anchored. Then as he clings for support to some tuft of herbage above, he suddenly finds in his hand a bunch of leaves which he has not seen before, and which he soon finds out belong to the Breidden plant *Potentilla rupestris*, unknown elsewhere but happily plentiful here, and growing where it is not likely to suffer greatly from the ravages of unprincipled collectors. And then, as ledge after ledge of rock comes into sight in his upward scramble, he rejoices in the exquisite contrast of two friends, often found together, and though each beautiful in itself yet each lending a new beauty to the other, the tufts and masses of *Geranium sanguineum*, with its large, graceful drooping crimson flowers, and the stiff, upright spikes of the dense cobalt-blue flowerets of the *Veronica spicata*. Here and there too are seen standing out stiffly from the rock-face three or four stems of the rare *Lychnis Viscaria*, crowned with its bunches of bright pink flowers. While over numberless little juts and ledges on every side hang the gay trailers of Rock-rose and *Sedum*, with their yellow flowers, or sometimes the larger and more beautiful flower-stems of the great ruddy-purple *Sedum Telephium*, or the green leafy foliage of the St John's-wort *(Hypericum Androsaemum)*."

Thus the Rev. W. W. How described the flora of Craig Breidden in *The Phytologist* in 1859 and he went on in the fashion of the time to pay proper tribute to the Creator for all the works of nature.

It was romantic accounts of this kind which lured me out from school on my bicycle to explore the rocky slopes of the same hill. At the time, as is normal with young people, a sense of adventure and the collector's instinct were uppermost in my mind; both were satisfied on Craig Breidden, for the more unusual plants are mostly to be found in pretty inaccessible places. I am glad to record that I was a collector of observations rather than specimens even then, and I was lucky enough to see almost all the rare plants described by How and other nineteenth century enthusiasts. One has to admit that most botanical rarities are as dull to look at as a Penny Black and it is only the specialist who sees beauty in them. But the plants of rocky places are often an exception, and I am sure that their beauty and their easy cultivation as garden plants were responsible for the near extinction of some of the Breidden rarities over the past century.

FIGURE 5. The rock cinquefoil, an extremely rare plant in Britain, known only from eastern Wales.

I never found the rock cinquefoil *(Potentilla rupestris)*; seventeen years elapsed before I was shown a solitary survivor of the once flourishing colony by Mr Frank Best who was then the Forestry Commission's Conservator for North Wales. He and I were both concerned to save what was left of the glorious flora of Craig Breidden before it was too late.

PLATE 10. Aerial view of part of Breidden Hill, Montgomeryshire, from the south, showing extensive new quarrying operations and some undamaged crags.

The Breidden Hills (properly spelt Breiddin) are neither high nor extensive, but they form a striking landmark as one approaches Wales across the Shropshire Plain. It is their steepness rather than their size which makes them stand out among the gentler hills around them. Breidden Hill itself is just over 1200 ft high and is topped by a monument to Admiral Rodney. With the neighbouring summits of Moel-y-Golfa and Middletown Hill it forms a group of peaks which look like three extinct volcanoes. They are not, though the rocks from which they are formed were associated with volcanic activity. Breidden Hill and the lower ridges near it are composed of an igneous rock called dolerite, which was originally intruded in the molten state into the surrounding masses of Ordovician sediments. Dolerite is a basic rock: that is to say, it has a fairly high content of compounds of elements such as calcium, magnesium and iron. In this it resembles basalt rather than the acid granite which forms, for instance, the barren uplands and tors of Dartmoor.

The Breidden dolerite is peculiar in a number of ways and there can be little doubt that some of these peculiarities are in part responsible for the unique vegetation it supports. It is unusually rich in lime; pockets and veins of crystalline calcium carbonate are found scattered through the rock.

Breidden Hill is very steep on all sides except the east and there are numerous cliffs and smaller rock outcrops where little stable soil has accumulated. The southern and western slopes are parched by the summer sun. While the deeper soils and rock crevices support a great variety of trees, those areas where the soil is shallow and liable to drought bear a more open vegetation and have probably done so ever since the end of the Ice Age. It is on these barren slopes and ledges that most of the unusual plant communities are found. Almost certainly the persistence of open areas here through the period of maximum forest cover in prehistoric times provided a refuge for a number of small sun-demanding plants which may have been much commoner on the open wastes of early Post-glacial times. As Breidden Hill demonstrates, it is not only the cliffs of higher mountains like those in Snowdonia which provided such refuge areas.

The botanist on his first visit may not find any of the real rarities, but his eye is likely to be caught immediately by another peculiar feature: the magnificent clash, in colour as well as in ecological preference, of the flowers which dominate the cliff edges. Here the pinks and purples of ling and bell heather are intimately mixed with the magenta flowers of bloody cranesbill and the yellows of the common rockrose, rock stonecrop (Sedum forsteranum) and greater mouse-ear hawkweed (Pilosella peleterana). In their more familiar habitats some of these plants avoid lime-rich soils, while others appear to require lime in substantial quantities. This kind of mixture is not unique to Breidden but most of the other places where it occurs have a thin layer of acid lime-free soil overlying calcareous material. On Breidden the roots of the various plants, and the soil components, appear to be intimately mingled. Apart from the hawkweed, the rarer plants are not scattered throughout these communities but occur very locally. The red catchfly *(Lychnis viscaria)* and the spiked speedwell

FIGURE 6. The red German catchfly, a rare plant in Britain, known only from Scotland and eastern Wales.

(Veronica spicata) appear to favour certain sites whose soils dry out in summer, and are often associated with a number of winter annuals such as shepherd's cress *(Teesdalia nudicaulis)* which carry out all their active growth in the cooler and moister winter months. The rock cinquefoil *(Potentilla rupestris)* has become so scarce that it is difficult to generalise about its requirements, but in its other British localities it is found in damper situations than those prevailing on Craig Breidden today.

An odd feature of this association of rarities at Breidden is the fact that each of them has a distinct geographical range in Britain and Europe bearing little resemblance to the others and that they only come together in the Welsh Borderland. The peculiarities of Craig Breidden are to some extent repeated at Stanner Rock in Radnorshire, whose geology is rather similar. Stanner, however, lacks the *Potentilla rupestris* and has the common mouse-ear hawkweed in place of *Pilosella peleterana*.

Craig Breidden was first mentioned botanically as 'Craig Wreidhin' by Edward Lhuyd, the famous Welsh botanist, in a letter to John Ray dated 1689. Lhuyd was responsible for the first British records of *Lychnis, Potentilla* and *Veronica* from this site. The Hill subsequently became a regular haunt of botanists in an otherwise neglected region. It was their over-enthusiasm as collectors which first seriously threatened the survival of some of the rarer species — by the early years of this century there were more *Potentilla rupestris* plants in the Vicarage garden at Criggion than on the Hill itself — but recently another and greater danger has arisen.

Unfortunately the peculiar properties of Breidden dolerite are not confined to their effect on soils and plants. The part of the Hill which How and his contemporaries knew as the Black Rock has long since disappeared in a quarry, now forming one of the highest man-made rock faces in Britain. Quarrying on a limited scale took place in the earlier decades of this century, but recently the rock has been found to have unique qualities as a road surfacing material: its durability and especially its resistance to polishing make it one of the best non-slip materials available and it is much in demand for the top veneer on motorways and other roads. This dolerite is of a very attractive greenish colour and it has also become popular with architects for the facing of buildings. Not only has the original quarry face eaten deeply into the western side of the hill but new workings have recently been opened at the southern end (Plate 10). Criggion Quarry is now managed by the Amalgamated Roadstone Corporation, and its output runs into several hundred thousand tons per year. It is important to remember that besides being a flourishing commercial enterprise a quarry of this kind provides a most important service to the community at large. The rest of the hill is in the hands of the Forestry Commission, who have planted it extensively wherever the gradient and soil permit. The same is true of Stanner Rock where there is no active quarrying at the moment.

Interest in the flora of Craig Breidden apparently waned during the years between the Wars, a doldrum period for amateur naturalists generally. Apart from a handful of local naturalists, there seem to have been few people interested in Craig Breidden until the early nineteen-fifties. Miss V. J. Macnair and her colleagues in Montgomeryshire kept a watchful eye on the hill, as did Mr Frank Best of the Forestry Commission. It was he who collected and sowed seed from the last surviving plant of *Potentilla rupestris*. Some of this seed has now germinated on ledges not far from the original plant, and there is a good chance of the colony re-establishing itself.

The hill was declared a Site of Special Scientific Interest by the Nature Conservancy in the early fifties, but originally on grounds of its geological interest alone. When its botanical importance was brought to their attention the North Wales office of the Conservancy took active steps to negotiate some kind of conservation agreement with the quarry management and I was involved in these discussions from the start. The quarry management (and notably its local manager, Mr Lloyd) have been exceptionally co-operative, taking full account of the conservation interest in the working out of their short-term and long-term plans of operation. In recent years Mr Lloyd has been in touch with me on every occasion when new workings threatened interesting parts of the site, and in almost every case it has been possible to find a mutually satisfactory solution to the problem.

Inevitably large parts of the cliffs and screes have had to be removed, for the best quality of rock occurs in just those places where the interesting plant communities are found. I am convinced, however, that much more has been achieved by careful and moderate negotiation, and above all by explaining the exact nature and extent of the scientific interest of the site, than could possibly have been done by outright opposition to a reputable and productive enterprise.

Meanwhile, as a secondary precaution against the local extinction of rare plants, the North Wales Naturalists' Trust arranged to rent a small and rocky part of the hill from the Forestry Commission. This site lacked most of the rarities but garden-reared plants of some of them have been transplanted here. Although this Reserve is on the same rock, its local climate is very different from the original sites and it is too early to say whether this attempt to establish the plants will be permanently successful. A watchful eye is kept on the Reserve by a small Committee of local naturalists.

Arguing the relative merits of nature conservation and commerce with hard-headed business men is difficult enough at the best of times. To my mind it is vital to convince people not only that a site is interesting but also that an active interest is being taken in it. Thanks to popular articles by Mr P. W. Carter, Mr S. J. Turner and others, interest in the Breidden flora has re-awakened in recent years. Because of the need to consolidate this interest and to build up a more detailed knowledge of the ecology of the unusual plant communities before too much of the hill was quarried away, I applied for and received from the Natural Environment Research Council in 1967 a research grant to study the vegetation and soils of dolerite outcrops on Craig Breidden. A Research Assistant, Mr S. C. Jarvis, was appointed and has now nearly completed his studies with results of outstanding interest. He too has enjoyed the full co-operation of the quarrying company. The results of his work will be published in due course, but it can already be said that some of the causes of the unique ecological character of Craig Breidden are better understood.

There is now good reason to hope that the really important parts of these classic crags will survive, together with the curious plant communities and the rare species which they carry. It is also not unlikely that many of the plants will have the opportunity to *re-colonise* abandoned parts of the quarry workings in due course and so to extend the area of interest.

At the present time most of the area is very dangerous and difficult of access — perhaps this is no bad thing. Permission should always be sought from the quarry company through me or the North Wales Trust before a visit is made.

Stanner Rock is rather less well known and less at risk. It is hoped that arrangements between the Herefordshire and Radnorshire Nature Trust and the Forestry Commission will ensure conservation of the similar plant communities there. Meanwhile any new information on the site is welcome. Permission is again required for visiting it.

Nature conservation is a philosophy, an attitude of mind. Those of us who believe in it and wish to see it more effectively pursued, whether we work for official bodies such as the Nature Conservancy or in a voluntary way through our local Trusts, are convinced of one thing: it is only by explaining our attitude reasonably and by understanding the other person's point of view that we are ever likely to see the day when the wise use and management of our whole environment gains the priority it deserves.

XIX

TOWYN BURROWS, CARMARTHENSHIRE

MRS I. M. VAUGHAN, M.B.E., F.L.S.

Welsh Region, Botanical Society of the British Isles

Towyn Burrows comprise the northern portion of some 5000 acres of sand dunes lying between the estuary of the Gwendraeth river running up to Kidwelly, once a busy port under the wing of its noble 13th century castle, and another by-passed and disused port at Pembrey in the south. This great area of multiform environments, sandy shores, fore dunes, secondary dunes, open fixed dunes, dune slacks, and saltings must, in its pristine state, have been 'paradise enow' for naturalists and still remains the richest in the county for its wonderful range of plants and animals. Its potentialities are as yet quite largely unexplored.

Since 1934 some 3000 acres have been planted by the Forestry Commission, mainly with Corsican pine, with occasional stands of Sitka and Norway spruce and, more rarely, maritime pine. Though it is true that the open rides of the forest have given sanctuary to many species of plants and animals and constitute an entomological treasury, yet some specialised species have been restricted or lost in their former stations. As the thinning of the plantations proceeds and light is admitted increasingly to the ground layer, it should be of great interest to see what may return, or what may newly colonise the changed habitat: whether, for instance, the spurges *(Euphorbia paralias* and *E. portlandica)* here just holding on to the edges of pine clad secondary dunes, re-establish themselves or whether their place will be taken by the woodland spurge *(Euphorbia amygdaloides)* present in near-by coppices. Will the hairy violet *(Viola hirta)*, last seen about 1956, return? Will roedeer join the numerous foxes and badgers in the forest and will red squirrels be seen again? All these questions and very many more must be seen in a new context of urgency since the whole area may be taken over in the near future by the Ministry of Defence. It could well be that the protection afforded by restriction of public access would preserve a number of habitats extremely vulnerable by their very nature to trampling and disturbance but some loss must also ensue. Changes with loss and gain are inevitable conditions of life, but commercial exploitation would be vastly worse.

A more natural menace to plant life is the locally dense coverage of sea buckthorn *(Hippophae rhamnoides)* planted at about the same date as the pines. This shrub not only reproduces by abundant seed but also by profuse suckering, which of couse is the reason for its introduction as a sand binder. Like so many well-intentioned introductions its rapacity and its density give it dominance over all lesser herbage. Its lovely orange berries are doubtful recompense for its suppression of native species and its thorns which make such painful passage.

The area to the north of the afforestation was, until recently, the site of an R.A.F. aerodrome and training station. A bombing range is still retained in the area between the planted forest, the estuarine salt-marsh, and the notorious Cefn Sidan sands with their history of wrecking gangs and pillage. Part of this area, which includes salt-marsh and the best of the dunes and slacks, has long been a proposed National Nature Reserve awaiting release from the Air Ministry. Inshore of this the aerodrome itself has been sold to Messrs Eastwood for factory chicken production. These varied curbs on full access have undoubtedly preserved what remains of the natural dune complex from further exploitation though the new usages have inevitably been harmful to some species. White-fronted geese *(Anser albifrons albifrons)* used to flight here in winter but their favourite pool was drained by the Forestry Commission and they have found the overhead disturbance intolerable, so come no more. The absence of these winter grazers has probably altered the composition of the grass-sedge swards. The charming ringed plover *(Charadrius hiaticula hiaticula)* seems unperturbed on the shore but the greater number of the waders favour the Pembrey end of the territory rather than the estuary end where the low tides bare the sands for a mile out. Montagu's harriers *(Circus pygargus)* have been reported intermittently over a number of years but are not known to have bred.

The foredunes here are subject to considerable ' blow-outs ' and recolonization of these areas of natural devastation takes place from time to time. The re-establishment of first colonists such as sand couch-grass *(Agropyron junceiforme)*, sea couch-grass *(Agropyron pungens)* and sand sedge *(Carex arenaria)*, the whole process of succession, and the problem of the survival of out-blown inshore plant material would all make most interesting ecological studies. Lyme grass *(Elymus arenarius)*, of which only one clump was known some fifteen years ago as a first county record, is now increasing in open dunes fronting both sea and estuary, its vertical dignity in strong contrast to the horizontal scurry of the hybrid cord-grass, sparsely evident at the same date but now spreading rapidly into the salt marsh to the suppression of all else of greater interest.

There seems to be evidence of a falling water table, not only in the zones of actual afforestation, but over the whole area. Little shallow pools in damp sandy open habitats well inland of the dune slacks are drying out; here used to be the coastal water buttercup (*Ranunculus baudottii*) and the lesser water plantain (*Baldellia ranunculoides*). The *Ranunculus* had disappeared in 1969 and the *Baldellia* was reduced to half-dried remnants. In this area too is an abundance of the small-fruited yellow sedge (*Carex serotina*) which with the spike rushes (*Eleocharis uniglumis* and *E. quinqueflora*) may be in danger of extinction.

Taking a line from the planted or ploughed area and walking northwards across the R.A.F. bombing reservation the first and greatest feature is the wealth of orchids. The marsh helleborine (*Epipactis palustris*), sometimes in almost pure sward, and the marsh orchids (*Dactylorhiza praetermissa, D. purpurella* and *D. incarnata*), make a real vision of delight. The pyramidal orchid (*Anacamptis pyramidalis*) is abundant near the upper observation tower and intermittent over the drier parts of the region: here too occur the autumn lady's tresses (*Spiranthes spiralis*), and the green-winged orchid. The fragrant orchid is generally sparse on the dunes but sometimes occurs in a stand of over 100 plants: the bee orchid (*Ophrys apifera*), elusive and enchanting, is there if you can find it. In the wetter dune slacks which are not too densely populated by the variegated horsetail (*Equisetum variegatum*) or by the creeping willow, the rare fen orchid (*Liparis loeselii*) seems to be spreading, though an apparent increase may be only a discovery of previously unknown populations. The fen orchid (Plate 11) was first found here by A. E. Wade in 1930. In less damp conditions and very diffusely distributed, are two more rarities, dune felwort (*Gentianella uliginosa*) and the larger wintergreen (*Pyrola rotundifolia* ssp. *maritima*). Three species of centaury (*Centaurium littorale, C. pulchellum* and *C. erythraea*) show pink stars as foil to the white ones of the knotted pearlwort (*Sagina nodosa*).

Beyond the main dune slack area comes a zone which is dominated by the sharp rush (*Juncus acutus*), sea rush (*Juncus maritimus*), the mud rush (*Juncus gerardii*), and further inland, the blunt-flowered rush (*Juncus subnodulosus*), with abundant parsley water dropwort (*Oenanthe lachenalii*) and very occasional wild celery (*Apium graveolens*) and *Asparagus officinalis*.

Beyond this again is a zone which is almost pure sedge sward, mainly the long-bracted sedge (*Carex extensa*) and the distant sedge (*Carex distans*) with a little tawny sedge (*Carex hostiana*). North of this again the open salt marsh, guarded by a line of secondary dunes, has two sea lavenders *(Limonium vulgare* and *L. binervosum),* and a patchy sward of the usual saltmarsh communities, thrift *(Armeria maritima),* glasswort *(Salicornia* species), a spurrey *(Spergularia media),* sea plantain *(Plantago maritima),* sea arrow-grass *(Triglochin maritima),* sea purslane *(Halimione portulacoides),* sea poa *(Puccinellia maritima),* red fescue *(Festuca rubra)* and sea hard-grass *(Parapholis strigosa).*

The foredunes have a reservoir of species in open habitat which may often be found distributed elsewhere over the Burrows but which may be stifled by coarse grasses or scrub: two violets *(Viola canina* and *Viola tricolor* ssp. *curtisii)* the latter flowering almost continuously throughout the season, self-coloured or in every combination of blue and yellow; the highly successful evening primrose *(Oenothera* species), kidney vetch, the hairy hawkbit *(Leontodon taraxacoides)* and the ubiquitous ragwort *(Senecio jacobaea).* The grasses, besides the normal series up from the shore of sand couch to marram grass, are mainly spreading meadow grass *(Poa subcaerulea),* sand cat's-tail *(Phleum arenarium)* and dune fescue *(Vulpia membranacea).*

Inland again amongst the secondary dunes which are often thickly populated by the common polypody fern *(Polypodium vulgare)* are occasional stands of narrow-leaved everlasting pea *(Lathyrus sylvestris),* mounds as much as six feet across of coppery pea flowers, and sea bindweed *(Calystegia soldanella)* with pink funnels and fleshy reniform leaves. The stinking iris *(Iris foetidissima)* is local in isolated clumps on dry sand and the yellow flag iris *(Iris pseudacorus)* often dominant in swamps. One rather astonishing sight is a huge bush of the Japanese *Rosa rugosa,* a flaunting crimson invader, whereas the native burnet rose *(Rosa pimpinellifolia)* is here only a shy tenant of the southern forest rides. Other odd adventives in the rides are the false Acacia *(Robinia pseudacacia),* the holm oak *(Quercus ilex)* and wild pear *(Pyrus communis).* Peripheral ditches have great burdock *(Arctium lappa),* narrow-leaved water parsnip *(Berula erecta),* and horned pondweed *(Zannichellia palustris).* There is only one known specimen of sea wormwood *(Artemisia maritima).*

The bryophytes of the Burrows have been very little studied. Mosses include *Campothecium lutescens* which is prolific in semi-fixed wet habitats, *Tortula ruraliformis, Barbula tophacea,* and *Trichostomum flavovirens.* Two rather interesting hepatics are *Preissia quadrata* which makes quite a notable feature in the barer dune slacks and *Riccia crystallina* on open young dunes.

THE MYCOLOGICAL INTEREST OF THE AFFORESTED
PART OF TOWYN BURROWS

(S. N. Tallowin, Llandwry, near Kidwelly)

Pembrey forest provides an outstanding habitat for those interested in mycology. The habitat of a conifer forest on sand dunes has produced an abundance of fungi, including a number classified as 'rare' in the British Isles. The rides in the forest have produced the most interesting finds, and a detailed study of fungi of this area over a period of years would probably prove this to be one of the most valuable sites in the country from a mycologist's viewpoint.

List of the less common fungi found on four visits to Pembrey Forest: (R = rare, U = unusual)

Peziza nigrella	R	On conifer needles
Gloeophyllum sepiarium	U	Serious cause of conifer timber decay
Lactarius mitissimus	U	Under conifers
Lycoperdon ericetorum	U	Sandy places and heaths
Lepiota clypeolaria	U	On needle cover
Lepiota cristata	U	Paths in woods
Russula vesca	U	Woods generally
Russula cyanoxantha	U	Woods generally
Thelophora terrestris		On healthy soil and needle cover under conifers
Coltrichia perennis		Sandy soil in woods.

THE INSECT LIFE OF TOWYN BURROWS

(D. Davies, Rhandirmwyn)

The insect life of the dunes and afforested areas adds greatly to the pleasure and interest of the naturalist in Towyn Burrows for here are found species which are rare or absent elsewhere. Food plants for an interesting assembly of insects are afforded by the flora of the dunes, slacks, sea marshes, wide forest rides and firebreaks. In addition there are environmental factors, imperfectly understood, which favour the survival of insects in this particular ecosystem which are absent from other areas which would appear to be equally suitable.

As far as can be ascertained no detailed studies of the entomological fauna have been carried out in recent years. Most of the recent insect records for the Burrows have been made, almost incidentally, by botanists attracted by the extraordinarily interesting dune flora. As a consequence there are great gaps in our knowledge of the insects of Towyn and it is hoped that the fragmentary nature of the information contained in this account may provoke trained entomologists to visit the area and carry out proper surveys.

Twenty. four species of butterflies have been recorded in the past three years during two or three annual visits over the period. Sustained recording should result in additions to the list. There has been a grievous neglect of the moths.

A notable member of the butterfly fauna of the forest rides is the marbled white *(Melanargia galathea)*. A strong colony is present and there appears to be no great fluctuation in numbers from year to year. Since the marbled white feeds on common grasses in the larval stages its restriction to Towyn is not due to the absence of its food plant: although T. W. Barker *(Natural History of Carmarthen-*

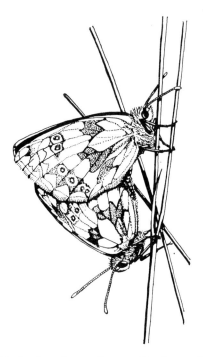

Figure 7: Marbled white butterflies at Pembrey, Carmarthenshire, 1969. The range of this species does not extend to North Wales.

shire, 1905*)* states that this species was ' somewhat local but abundant in places ' it is not now known elsewhere in the county. It has evidently found the environmental conditions at Towyn particularly well suited to its needs and, as a species at the extreme edge of its range, has adapted itself closely to the conditions obtaining there. If this local range has any physiological modifications then this has not obviously manifested itself in its colour or markings. The marbled white has only four functional legs instead of the usual six as the first pair are reduced to minute structures.

A provisional map showing the distribution of the small blue *(Cupido minimus)*, issued under the Lepidoptera Distribution Maps scheme in May 1968 and based entirely on records sent in to the scheme, shows two localities only for this species in Wales — Towyn Burrows and a site in Monmouthshire. It is probable that it occurs elsewhere in Wales but if so is a very local butterfly. Kidney vetch, the food plant of the caterpillar, is a dune plant at Towyn. Another member of the Lycaenidae which frequents the dunes and forest rides is the brown argus *(Aricia agestis)*. Rock rose and common storksbill, the food plants of this small attractive brown butterfly, both grow on the dunes.

The area affords habitats for two of the large handsome fritillaries. The dark green fritillary is on the wing in July, often perching on the tall thistles of the rides. Its larval food plant is the dog violet *(Viola canina)*, a dune plant at Towyn. The other is that swift high flyer, the silver washed fritillary. Sweet violet *(Viola odorata)* and dog violet are the listed food plants of this species. The dog violet is plentiful on the dunes but neither species grows in the extreme north of the county where this lovely fritillary is also found, so that other species of violet must be acceptable.

Before leaving the Lepidoptera it may be of interest to recall that the purple marbled moth *(Eublemma ostrina)* was recorded in 1865 as having been collected a few years previously at adjacent Pembrey. This is a North African and South European species so that the specimen observed at Pembrey was almost certainly an immigrant, although the food plant of the larva of this moth is said to be carline thistle, a common plant of these dunes.

The Coleoptera of the area are not without interest and would repay closer study. *Trichius fasciatus* is a hairy beetle with bold black and orange patterns so that it appears not unlike a bee when in flight. The mimicry displayed by the beetle is so effective that the common name for it is bee beetle. This Lamellicorn is said to occur especially on wild thyme, but the two specimens seen together on the Towyn salt marsh in June 1964 were on thrift. This is a local beetle of western Britain, many of the records coming from Snowdonia and Scotland. Yet this was not the first sighting of the beetle in the county for in 1905 Barker states: 'I have taken two specimens of the rare *Trichius fasciatus* in a garden on the Parade'. (This locality is in the town of Carmarthen).

Another beetle of limited distribution, found on the strand line at Cefn Sidan sands, is *Eurynebria complanata*. An account of this beetle appeared in Vol. 10 No. 1 *Nature in Wales*, March 1966.

What must be one of the earliest insect records for the area is referred to in an article which appeared in *The Field* on 15th April 1905, where an extract is given showing that the mole cricket *(Gryllotalpa gryllotalpa)* occupied marshes near Kidwelly in the year 1693 or thereabouts. This cricket has become exceedingly rare during the present century and the only recent records for it are from Hampshire and Surrey. It would be gratifying to know that it still survived in the water meadows or flood plains of this wonderful area.

XX

SOME PROBLEMS OF A NATURALISTS' TRUST IN INDUSTRIAL WALES

R. H. S. HATTON, M.A., AND H. J. HAMBURY, F.R.C.S.

Glamorgan County Naturalists' Trust

IN THE NINE YEARS of its existence the Glamorgan Trust has faced and overcome many difficult problems. This is not surprising, if one remembers that Glamorgan has no more than ⅓ of an acre space per head of population, compared to 1·08 acres per person in the whole of Britain and as much as 16 acres for each inhabitant of Radnorshire. Conflicts of economic, social, and general ecological import are likely to be particularly intense. The tensions generated are accentuated by Glamorgan's wealth of different environments sheltering an exceptionally large species diversity.

Against this background the various conservation bodies, the Nature Conservancy, National Trust and C.P.R.W. have achieved much, and the Glamorgan Trust has obtained no fewer than twenty-three nature reserves totalling some 850 acres. These holdings generate management and protection problems but the Trust also feels obliged to serve as 'the ecological conscience of the County', to watch over hedgerows and road verges, to be continuously on the look-out for new sources of pollution and reckless dissipation of scanty natural resources, to advise everywhere on ways and means to enhance or at least preserve the quality of life. Thus it is only natural that conflicts arise and the Trust has endeavoured to weather them without sacrificing its long-term aims of conservation and improvement of the environment.

AMENITY AND CAR PARKS

Few landscapes in Britain are of greater poignancy than Rhossili Bay at the western extreme of Gower. It is overlooked by Rhossili Downs, rising from the golden sweep of 2½ miles of beach to form a 600 ft high monadnock emblazoned by bell heather, gorse, vernal squill *(Scilla verna)*, each at their proper time. Sands and downs are welded together by a ledge of dunes and a strip of fields on a narrow platform, an integral part of this grandiose setting. The sands and the long waves make Rhossili Beach a desirable goal for summer visitors. Such is the extent of the beach that even on a crowded August Bank Holiday there are long stretches of emptiness, now a rare and coveted asset. The Downs belong to the National Trust, but the fields belong to various farmers. In 1969 the owner of the fields nearest to Rhossili gave parking facilities to motorists and at the height of the season some 500 cars came down a rough track filling the nearest quarter of the length of the ledge with a parking jumble. It could be foreseen that this would lead to the destruction of the delicate natural cover of the dune top and the soil of the ledge with its bloody cranesbill and vernal squill. In a short time it would drive a long wedge of destruction between beach and downs, wrecking this unique landscape where to date only the outer tip of a caravan camp at Hill End interferes with an otherwise still unspoiled landscape reaching from Worms' Head to Burry Holms.

The Glamorgan County Council have served an enforcement order and in 1970 parking anywhere in front of Rhossili Downs will not be allowed. Fortunately there are ample and relatively inconspicuous car parks available in Rhossili village and a few hundred yards of footpath will bring bathers and surf board riders easily to their beach. There remains the problem of the owner who is being denied a source of income from his fields similar to that enjoyed by the owners of the established parking facilities. This Trust feels that a fund should be officially established from which those owners who, in the interest of an Area of Outstanding Beauty such as Gower, are denied certain lucrative development permits, should be indemnified. The acquisition of freeholds at commercially acceptable purchase prices which this Trust is practising, leaving the original owner the right to continue his usage, provided it remains compatible with the reserve's need and overall interest of the Area of Outstanding Natural Beauty, is a policy which aims at giving the 1948 Act some badly needed teeth.

INDUSTRY, ROAD TRANSPORT, RECREATION AND A NATURE RESERVE

The problem of Kenfig Burrows and Kenfig Pool is probably the most involved one of all tasks the Trust has had to tackle. This is a system of sand dunes on the shores of the eastern approach to Swansea Bay, some 1600 acres containing a large shallow fresh water pool; the dunes have previously been shown to be extremely unstable, but a degree of settlement has now been obtained by a somewhat tenuous cover consisting mainly of marram and creeping willow. The area is of tremendous ecological interest as the calcareous sands nourish a great variety of interesting plants, some as rare as the fen orchid (Plate 11), yellow bird's-nest *(Monotropa hypopitys)* and shore dock *(Rumex rupestris)*. Whilst the colony of little terns disappeared long ago, occasional visiting merlin might breed again here if the area were fully protected. The pool is famed for its variety of winter visiting birds and also as the almost sole remaining refuge of the Welsh mudwort *(Limosella subulata)* a humble but pretty aquatic annual.

The difficulties of establishing this complex of diverse habitats as a reserve in the face of demands for space for the development of the immediately adjoining Steel Company of Wales and the resultant population pressure, with all that implies in terms of road and recreational needs, was so great that the Nature Conservancy abandoned the project in 1954 in spite of a recommendation by the Wild Life Conservation Committee that Kenfig Burrows should be a National Nature Reserve (Cmd. 7122, HMSO. 1947). Fortunately in 1956 the doyen of Welsh ornithologists, H. Morrey Salmon, was able to induce the Glamorgan County Council, with the advice of the Nature Conservancy, to propose Kenfig Burrows as a Local Nature Reserve. This was prevented by an ancient legal conflict between the Trustees of the Margam Estate and the Burgesses of Kenfig over the ownership, but more recently legal advice proffered by the Glamorgan Trust was accepted, namely that the conflict should be transferred from a dispute over ownership to a dispute over proceeds of sale. This cleared the way for active planning of the multi-purpose use of the area, due consideration being given to the legitimate aims of recreational interests of golf, water sports, etc. At this stage the discussions were again hindered as a result of permission being given for cutting a temporary road from the South Cornelly limestone quarries to the new harbour constructed at Port Talbot, which for some three miles runs just within the territory of the proposed reserve. The use of the road for the conveyance of materials for the new port has come to an end but this temporary way-leave has meanwhile been widened and surfaced in defiance of the planning consent. There were suggestions that the road should be retained in order to attract more industrial development to the neighbourhood; that it was too big a capital asset to destroy it; that it would be invaluable as an additional cross-country connection between the dormitory settlements to the east and the steel works, and an additional access to the iron ore port; but alternatives for all these contingencies are available to the north west of the proposed reserve. Its removal is a costly and destructive civil engineering operation which might do more harm than good to the contiguous botanically important dune slacks. The Trust have agreed

PLATE 11. *Above left,* adder's tongue fern and, *right,* fen orchid in Towyn Burrows, Carmarthenshire; *below left,* marsh gentian in Anglesey; *right,* bird's-nest orchid in Cilygroeslwyd Wood (N.W.N.T. Nature Reserve), near Ruthin, Denbighshire.

to merely sealing the road at either end, thus giving it a chance to be re-integrated into the dune landscape by sand being blown over it. Any place left bare can then be covered gently and expertly by conservation corps methods, fixing it eventually by planting marram grass, etc. For this essential step to be taken the final declaration of the reserve status of the Burrows is necessary and the Trust is pressing the County Council to proceed urgently with the financial arrangements needed, which they will support to the utmost of their resources.

A CITY'S RUBBISH TIPS AND THE FLOWERING RUSH

The loss of Cadoxton Pond on the outskirts of Cardiff exemplified the need for unremitting vigilance by all naturalists. It harboured a wealth of bird life and such unusual plants as lesser pondweed *(Potamogeton pusillus)*, ivy duckweed *(Lemna trisulca)* and a magnificent stand of flowering rush *(Butomus umbellatus)*. In July 1969 Dr Mary Gillham, the Trust's Scientific Secretary for east Glamorgan, found it ' on the verge of being engulfed by an enormous rubbish dump '. The spreading heads of delicate pink reared themselves bravely among the fringing bur-reed into the acrid fumes of burning filth, with petrol cans and the inevitable polythene bottles bobbing at their feet. A fortnight later the pool was gone. The men on the lorries who brought the garbage and those on the bulldozers who pushed it into the diminishing waters had thought it a pity to destroy ' that nice pink flower '; had even rescued bunches to take home to their wives. They did not know that this was one of the last two or three sites for this plant in the whole of Glamorgan, and probably the best of them, and that one of its few remaining sites in the adjacent county of Monmouthshire had disappeared under a sewage pump only the year before. All Mary Gillham could do was to improvise a rescue operation and a good number of plants was planted out in some thirteen sites in Cardiff's ornamental parks. This is better than nothing, but the natural habitat is lost for ever. Rubbish tips will probably be needed for some time yet, but there *are* better methods of processing all rubbish and disposing of it usefully.

IS EVERYONE AGAINST THE BADGER?

As this article is being drafted, news has come in of the gassing of badgers in one of the Trust's reserves. Michael Porter records instances of its destruction in Breconshire. How is this animal to be protected? The widely-spread reserves can only be occasionally visited by warden and members. The badger continues to be poisoned by poultry farmers and gassed and trapped by anyone who fancies it, and yet it has been shown that, apart from the occasional rogue, badgers do not take either game birds or their eggs or poultry. If this ' opportunity feeder ', as Ernest Neal calls him, takes the occasional egg or chick, surely he makes up for his disdemeanour by the quantity of rats and mice he eats, as well as of slugs and wasps. And who would deny the attractive animals (Plate 8) their vegetarian food items such as acorns and beech nuts? How can one get the few offenders amongst the farmers and the roaming youths emerging from the edges of the dormitory suburbs of our sprawling city to respect these harmless and attractive, playful denizens of the woods? Here is the greatest challenge to the Trust's educational enthusiasm, an arduous, heart-breaking job, but one which must be tackled.

A RARITY BECOMES A PEST

Broad Pool, a beautiful 4¼ acre pond situated on open ground beside the road in the centre of the Gower Peninsula, was the Trust's first nature reserve. One of its most attractive features was the beautiful fringed water-lily *(Nymphoides peltatum)* which at that time covered about one twelfth of the area of the pool. This is a rare as well as a beautiful plant, occurring in only four sites in South Wales, and was one of the reasons for the acquisition of the pool. However, it flourished so well that by 1968 it covered the entire pool. It had become detrimental to the existence of other plants and to some animals in the pool, apart from lessening the aesthetic aspect of the pool when water ceased to be visible. The Trust has not been blind to this situation and has for some years been attempting to find a satisfactory method of control. It was hoped that biological control by the larvae of the Chinamark moth would prove effective, but this has not been the case, in spite of an estimated eight million in the pool. All methods tried have been shown to have serious defects and the Trust has now embarked upon the arduous task of clearing by hand. As the pool contains some 250 tons of water-lily it will obviously be no mean task to clear and dispose of even half that quanity; and the clearance of three quarters is desirable. And this was the prize species with first priority for conservation!

CAN OYSTERCATCHERS AND COCKLE FISHERS LIVE TOGETHER?

In 1965 the National Trust bought Whiteford Burrows, Gower, and leased part of the property to the Nature Conservancy to form part of Whiteford N.N.R. The Glamorgan County Naturalists' Trust played an essential part in the purchase of the property and is represented, together with the National Trust and the Nature Conservancy, on the Advisory Management Committee.

The first of a number of hazards was a dispute concerning rights of way, especially vehicular, which had started even before the purchase of the property. Disputes of this type are nearly always lengthy and difficult. The second was the now famous oystercatcher controversy, which reached national proportions. This is not the place to consider the rights and wrongs of the case or to go into detail, but a brief outline will give some idea of the extent of the problem. The Burry Estuary contains a cockle-fishing industry and the Reserve is situated at the mouth of the estuary. Some years ago the landings of cockles decreased and quite reasonably, the advice of the Ministry of Agriculture Fisheries and Food was sought. After a period of research the Ministry suggested that the oystercatchers, which have at times numbered something in the region of 20 000 in the estuary, were a potential threat to the industry and should be drastically reduced in number. As the birds were on the protected list this needed Home Office approval and also a practical method of carrying it out. The method decided on was 'cannon netting', i.e., shooting nets over large flocks of roosting birds. The only site in the estuary where this could be done was at Whiteford Point, a part of the Reserve particularly dear to bird watchers. The National Trust, with the memories of seal culling in the Farnes Islands fresh in mind, gave permission for research but not for killing birds. The destruction of perhaps ten thousand beautiful birds on the protected list could hardly be a generally popular first use of a Nature Reserve; and even the idea of a research programme met with strong opposition in some quarters. Concern has been widespread and feelings have sometimes risen high during the last four years. At times the Trust's telephone lines have been congested with calls from private individuals, members of ornithological and protection societies, wildfowlers, R.S.P.C.A., local and national press, television and broadcasting companies and government departments. There is clearly no easy solution to this problem, though the birds themselves are at present doing their best to solve the problem by refusing to roost where they can be caught!

THE DISASTROUS EFFECTS OF AN ADVENTIVE PLANT SPECIES

In the early 1930's the Forestry Commission planted one square chain of sea buckthorn at Towyn Burrows on the north side of the Burry Estuary in order to stabilise shifting sands. Mrs. Vaughan has drawn attention to the menace of this species in Section XIX which has spread to 4000 acres, much of it impenetrable. Many of the starlings which visit Gower roost in the woods at Towyn and feed on the berries of the sea buckthorn and there is little doubt that these birds have carried the seeds across the estuary and introduced the species to Whiteford. The flora of the dune slacks, a very valuable part of the Reserve, was clearly threatened by the spread of the sea buckthorn and as soon as the Reserve was established a survey of the species and experimental research into methods of control were undertaken. It was found that there were already some 10 000 plants spread over thirty-seven dune slacks, increasing rapidly and already dense in places. The use of herbicides was found to be impractical, as was uprooting, due to the damage caused to surrounding rare species. When a plant was cut down the rhizome quickly produced several more plants, but when these in turn were cut the plant's vitality was gradually lessened. This is the method being used and it is hoped that in several years' time when perhaps 100 000 plants have been cut, the problem will have been solved!

COMMENT

Enough has been said to show that not everything in the conservation garden is lovely, or, to use a metaphor from recreation, the work of a Naturalists' Trust is far from being all plain sailing. The acquisition of nature reserves is the least of a Trusts' problems; the real work begins with the management of the Reserves, with their effective utilization for protective or educational purposes, and with representation directed in the most suitable quarters aimed at securing satisfactory integration of the various kinds of land-use.

These and many more tasks must go on and when the enthusiasm at present shared by the comparatively few fires the imagination of the very many as yet uncommitted, then with patient persistence, with tolerance and with a new co-operation on all sides resulting from a better understanding of land-use problems, then and only then will the efforts to secure the Welsh countryside unspoiled for future generations be crowned with success. That this new co-operation has already begun is evidenced by the Lower Swansea Valley Project described by Gordon Goodman in the following Section.

XXI

THE LOWER SWANSEA VALLEY: A TEXT FOR THE CONSERVATIONIST*

GORDON T. GOODMAN, M.SC.

Glamorgan County Naturalists' Trust

' *The Lower Swansea Valley today is a stark monument to thought-less and ruthless exploitation, and while it remains in its present state it is a standing reproach to each generation which shrugs its shoulders and looks the other way. . . . It is so easy to justify desecration and pollution in the name of progress, it is so simple to lay ruthless hands on the unresisting countryside in the name of the national interest. It is nothing like such a simple matter to clear up the mess afterwards.*'

The Duke of Edinburgh

ONE OF THOSE UNCOMFORTABLE THOUGHTS that seem to crop up with ever increasing regularity these days is the disquieting prospect of the human race irreversibly contaminating its global environment. For modern man now has the technological power to master and control the old, naturally-evolving world of living things of which, until fairly recently, he formed a somewhat insignificant part. Soon perhaps, even the rather terrifying ' noosphere' suggestion made by Vernadsky in 1945, will begin to appear plausible. Shall we ever really replace the old biosphere by a world of living things dominated by the mind of man? Will our children inherit this ' noosphere', a sort of global theatre where man arranges all the environmental scenes, chooses the biological cast and produces the ecological play?

Of course, if men are wise enough to understand the results of all their activities in the environment, then we have nothing to fear. But the evidence of human fecklessness accumulates year by year with a persistence which it is very hard to ignore, even by those of us who still have faith in man as a rational creature. One begins to wonder

* Reprinted, with permission, from the Glamorgan County Naturalists' Trust *Bulletin* No. 8, 1969, pp. 10-16 and revised by the author.

whether the 'environmental backlash' situations which have arisen in the 1960's from such human activities as the use of pesticides and antibiotics in agriculture, mercury in Sweden or even lead shot in the U.S.A., represent the tip of an iceberg whose dimensions are as yet uncharted by our environmental scientists.

All these are of course global problems which the world's scientific community are slowly beginning to notice, and you may be wondering what this gloomy prognosis has to do with the Lower Swansea Valley? The fact is that the creation of derelict land in Swansea during the nineteenth century, as in the rest of Britain, is a text-book example of man's earlier contamination of his environment which is still for the most part unrepaired, the 'backlash' lesson as yet unlearned.

Many of us are so familiar with the 1200 acres of derelict landscape immediately to the north of Swansea that we take it for granted and our eyes look beyond the bare gullied slopes, black waste heaps and crumbling buildings of a decayed industry to pleasanter more distant views. But it comes as a brutal shock to a visitor and is so repellent to any would-be developer that the land remains unused, neglected and unsightly.

This familiar pattern is reflected elsewhere in England and Wales where the Ministry of Housing and Local Government has estimated that there were 127 000 acres of 'land so damaged by industrial or other development that it is incapable of further use without treatment', i.e. about 0·25% of the land surface. The Hunt Committee, reporting in 1969, reckoned dereliction as covering 93 000 acres of England and 37 000 acres of Scotland and Wales. A commonly accepted figure for the rate of production of derelict land in England and Wales is about 3500-4000 acres per annum. These rather low figures are seen in truer perspective when it is realized that nearly all our derelict land is in and around the large centres of population, so that it has the maximal influence over the greatest number of people.

Apart from the general unsightliness of derelict land, the waste tips on it may burn spontaneously, emitting noxious gases, and since tips revegetate only very slowly, if at all, they are subject to wind and water erosion. Thus, blown dust can be a health hazard and/or a nuisance, especially near housing, and its chemical constituents, particularly from old metalliferous wastes, may depress crop yields when blown onto surrounding agricultural land. Similarly, water-borne tip material may pollute and silt up streams and rivers, causing flooding; soluble chemical contaminants seeping out of tips may poison watercourses for decades. In some cases, fortunately very rare, tips may become mechanically unstable and may slide, if they do not drain freely (e.g. the Aberfan tip disaster of 21st October 1966).

This ugly, abandoned land attracts 'fly-tippers' who dump their old cars or any other noisome rubbish, often adding vermin to the prevailing squalor. All these nuisances inhibit the proper re-use of derelict land. This is the ' back-lash ' plain for all to see and well re-presented in the Lower Swansea Valley.

Perhaps all this has been greatly exaggerated? We hear that, ' where there's muck there's brass ', so we cannot afford to be too squeamish. The ' hard-economic-facts ' school of thought often takes the view that the inhibiting effect of dereliction on redevelopment is nonsense, on the principle, perhaps, that what cannot be measured does not exist. But any seasoned planning officer knows from experience that developers want high quality sites, and will avoid taking up old industrial eyesores. In fact, it is often realized that for every one acre of truly derelict land, there will be another ten surrounding it whose future development will be impaired. These problems have been well understood by successive governments who have provided grant-aid to clear derelict land. The current Acts (Local Government Act, 1966, and Industrial Development Act, 1966) provide eligible local authori-ties with up to about 85% of the cost of clearance and/or treatment, providing that as a result the growth of industry and/or housing is stimulated. Reclamation for amenity use is only encouraged where failure to do so would deter industrial development or jeopardize public safety.

If grant aid exists on this scale one might wonder what the problems were which have prevented Swansea from clearing its derelict land forthwith? Of course there have been many problems; the land was privately owned and legislation has not always been so favourable as it is now. Indeed when one reviews the history of earlier legislation, one can hardly escape the feeling that for Swansea, at least, successive parliaments had given every possible assistance short of actual help! Certainly the situation in the 1950's looked as static as it had been for years despite real efforts by the local Authority to get things moving.

It was in this rather bleak climate that, in 1960, the University College of Swansea set up a Working Group to raise money to start a fact-finding study of the Lower Swansea Valley problem. Heads of the various College departments were joined by representatives of the Borough Council, local industry and the Welsh Office, and due to their efforts, grants totalling nearly £49 000 were generously given by the Borough Council, the Ministry of Housing, local industry, and the Department of Scientific and Industrial Research, with the Nuffield Foundation providing almost half of the total sum.

With the finance assured, the Working Group set up sub-committees, a Director (K. J. Hilton) was appointed in the autumn of 1961, and work began in earnest in 1962 on what became known as the Lower

153

Swansea Valley Project. The terms of reference were 'to establish the factors which inhibit the social and economic use of land in the Lower Swansea Valley and to suggest ways in which the area should be used in the future'. Many of the University departments were in a good position to contribute to this study because they had expert staff and specialist equipment whose services would be given free of charge. Where specialist assistance was required, temporary University researchers were engaged for the duration of the investigation. Although a good deal has now been written about this unusual multidisciplinary study, it is not always fully understood that the Project team could never have hoped to do the actual job of reclamation, involving the building of roads, bridges, parks, etc. No University is equipped for a large scale engineering programme of this sort which would involve far more money than had been donated. The investigation had to be confined to preparing a blue-print for future action. In practice, the Project's activities turned out to be a physical and socio-economic study of how the Valley came to be the industrial desert it is today, what would be the most effective and practicable uses to which the Valley could be put in the future, what detailed technical knowledge was required to achieve this and how much it would all cost.

As a beginning, the industrial history of the Swansea Valley was studied and a detailed case history of derelict land in Swansea was prepared. This showed that starting from as early as 1717, copper, followed by zinc and iron-smelting, using locally mined coal, as well as a tinplate industry all contributed to make Swansea a world metallurgical centre during the late 19th century. In the 1870's this employed about 10 000 people of Welsh, Irish, English, German and Belgian origin. Working and living conditions were very hard for the men, women and children employed in the Valley and many died in the epidemics of cholera and other diseases which frequently swept through Morriston and Llansamlet. This unwanted human side effect was accompanied by another; the toxic sulphurous fumes produced by the non-ferrous smelting industry killed all the vegetation on the adjoining Valley sides and laid bare the top-soil, which was then washed down on to the Valley floor where, together with the large, growing tips of smelter waste, it impeded drainage and caused flooding problems. The bare sub-soil of the Valley slopes remains largely devoid of vegetation to this day. This great industry began to wane after about 1880, and declined rapidly after World War I, until most of the Valley was deserted.

A physical study of the Valley was begun by geologists and mechanical engineers from the University, who made maps of the solid geology and drift deposits in the area and investigated the risk of subsidence from landslips and old mine shafts. The load-bearing characteristics of the heaps of copper, zinc and steel waste were studied, in case factories and heavy industrial plant had to be sited on the tips during some future building phase. A micro-contour map made by the geographers from special air-photographs enabled the engineers to calculate the volume of tip material in the Valley and thus to fix a height down to which all the tips could be bulldozed so that the surplus removed material would just fill any hollows between the tips to create a level platform for development. A hydrologist drew up a detailed plan for reducing the flood risk in the Valley. It was suggested that the River Tawe, not suitable as a water resource for industry, could be a valuable water amenity if a moveable 'fabri-dam' barrage were to be placed near the New Cut Bridge so as to prevent the lower reaches of the River from being tidal. This would flood the river, submerging the unsightly tidal banks of the Tawe up to Morriston.

An ecological study of the heavy-metal contaminated soils and waste heaps by a small team from the Botany Department, assisted by the National Agricultural Advisory Service, produced inexpensive techniques for growing grass, trees and shrubs in these toxic materials. This study was important for two reasons. It was shown by the sociologists that eastern Swansea was very badly off for amenity open space. It had three times less than west Swansea (2·4 acres, compared with 7·3 acres/1000 people: recommended national average for playing fields alone is 6 acres/1000 people). Thus the need to create parks, playing-fields and other open space in any future development plan was very pressing. The second reason was that planning authorities in other parts of U.K., notably Lancashire, had discovered that derelict land which had remained unsold for development was quickly taken up as soon as it was given a 'face-lift' by planting trees or grass. The trees and grass thus planted may not necessarily be permanent, but only a way of stimulating properly regulated re-use of the land. This pointed to the need for some form of 'cosmetic planting' in the Valley. People living in and around derelict land feel a sense of hopelessness that nothing can ever be done to improve their environment and rather fatalistically come to accept it. All this changes when patches of green begin to appear here and there; the local community begins to show interest in its surroundings once more. For these two reasons, the Project departed from its purely fact-finding remit when a University forester working with the ecological team planted 100 000 trees in collaboration with the Forestry Commission. Although some twenty-six different species were used, they were chiefly: Japanese larch, lodgepole pine, birch, Corsican pine and alder, and were confined to conspicuous places on the less toxic sites; in all, some sixty acres. Today the trees are growing well and arouse a good deal of interest among the local community.

In a way, this large-scale tree planting was an act of faith because everyone said they would be destroyed by fire or vandalism, and of course this could still happen. Right from the outset, however, the forester embarked on a regular programme of talks and practical work on tree planting and tree-care as well as visits to nearby Forestry Commission woodlands with the local schools and youth groups. This work has received invaluable support from the Reverend Ted Hunt and has been enthusiastically welcomed by the local young people, who may often work for their Duke of Edinburgh Awards via this tree-protection scheme. As a direct result of this, our vandalism losses have been unbelievably low in contrast to other town-woodland schemes. Fires frequently occur in the Valley, often started by people burning rubbish or firing grass to control vermin, but the local youth group's fire-watching service calls the fire-brigade and usually manages to extinguish the blaze without further help. We could still have one big fire which would undo all the good work, so the vigilance must continue. To this end, the Local Authority have paid the salary of the forester in latter years. This exercise has pioneered a completely new approach to vandalism. There are no costly barbed-wire fences to maintain, only the confidence and interest of the young people, which anyway is a good investment for future attitudes to the countryside and woodlands among the towns-people of the next few decades.

There are no proper roads in the Lower Valley and a detailed road and traffic survey by a communications engineer established 'desire-lines' for an improved road system. A strong case was made for improving access to the Swansea area by widening the present Neath Valley road (A465) and extending the M4 to Llanelli. It was clear that the present roads encircling the Lower Valley should also be widened and footpaths made from existing residential areas to any new amenity open space on the Valley floor, where a new road network was mapped out. Two new bridges were also recommended.

Obviously the most important single factor in the Valley is the people who live in it, roughly a quarter of the population of the County Borough. The sociologists discovered that the people who lived in the Valley were not, as has often been discreetly rumoured, those who found it less demanding to live there rather than compete for a place in west Swansea. By all the usually accepted sociological criteria, they were a normal cross-section of the population of the County Borough (apart from a shortage of some of the most wealthy groups), living in a sub-standard environment as regards public buildings, schools and housing. Because the north and eastern parts of the Lower Valley are convenient places to live in for travel to work in the industrial areas of Llanelli, Neath or Port Talbot, younger people are moving into these parts and the Valley population is not declining. There is a great need for more housing in the future, some of which could be sited on the Valley floor. A good deal of new open space was also required; two new parks, a river walk, an adventure playground and bicycle track for youngsters, as well as free open space were all recommended. It was suggested that the Lower Valley would be an excellent place to site an indoor winter recreational centre as part of a regional plan for sport.

The economists examined the possible long-term economic trends in Swansea as part of the likely future development of the south west Wales sub-region. Because of the considerable unemployment which we are likely to face in the future, the growth of new jobs would have to be stepped up to provide work for 30-40 000 people by 1981. Thus, more long-term and selective inducements for firms to settle here are required. The future industrial use of the Lower Valley is linked to having an effective overall policy for industrial growth in the sub-region and in the absence of this, it is unlikely that a comprehensive industrial redevelopment of the Valley will occur.

Many other studies were made, e.g., on climate, air-pollution and the incidence of respiratory complaints among residents in the Lower Valley; and a great many people helped to foster the Project in all sorts of ways. All the detailed facts and figures contributed in the report of each of the investigators were sifted, and a master development-plan was drawn up, which it was hoped would replace the existing plan of zoning the whole Valley for industry. Under the new plan, a multipurpose use of the floor of the Lower Valley was envisaged, with 407 acres of industrial and commercial development (including the possibility of taking not more than 110 acres of this for new housing, a sports centre and a school). A further 115 acres was earmarked for new housing and another 120 acres for amenity. It was suggested that the new industry should not be fume-producing and that the whole redevelopment should be an integrated exercise, considering industry, housing and amenity all together. Obviously, when the detailed proposals were finally agreed by the Local Authority, they could only be implemented a piece at a time until the whole job was finished. Therefore, it was recommended that those areas not scheduled for early redevelopment should be temporarily improved by cosmetic landscaping and the existing trees already planted by the Project, maintained.

The economists then costed the whole operation as far as possible, and finally computed this as of the order of £3 000 000. It was thought that any authority developing the whole area would get a good return on its investment in the long term.

All the factual evidence was assembled in technical reports, from which the final report, 'The Lower Swansea Valley Project', was prepared and published in 1967 (edited by K. J. Hilton, Longmans Green, London), and where the nature of the argument is presented in straightforward terms for all to read and evaluate.

The Lower Swansea Valley is now the most intensively studied bit of landscape in the world. With the appearance of the Report in 1967 the Project was over and the University's role largely fulfilled. Two years have passed. So far as is known the Report has not yet been formally accepted by anybody. Will all the work simply be a waste of time and money — just one more chapter in the history of difficulty and frustration which has been the hallmark of our national attitude to dereliction since before the thirties? There are now some grounds for optimism. It usually takes an Aberfan or a *Torrey Canyon* to stir our national awareness, and these disasters have been a watershed in the nation's thinking about pollution. It now seems that Government money will be forthcoming; the Borough Council have been able to clear the White Rock tip and retain a firm of professional engineering consultants to cost out in detail the various ideas of the Report.

In the past it was not nearly as easy as it is now for the public to influence land-use. So if the Valley is not now redeveloped in the way we want it to be, it will be our fault; for this time, it is quite certain that we shall get the kind of Valley that we deserve.

Let us hope that all of us will take such an interest in the progress of the restoration of the Lower Valley that the spirit of the redevelopment will be honoured: '*The vision of the future is of a valley in which people live and play as well as work, without these activities intruding much on each other; a valley which offers the seclusion of wooded slopes and quiet paths as well as the activity of its workshops; a valley where the sides and floor are brought together, not only in the daily journey to work as in the past, but for shopping and for entertainment, for walks along the river bank, for games and for school; a valley which instead of dividing the Borough, unites it in a new focus of landscape beauty, enjoyment and employment. This is a vision which is quite capable of becoming a reality with the local and regional resources which are available provided that a determined effort is made to achieve it.*' (K. J. Hilton).

XXII

PROCEEDINGS OF THE FIRST CONFERENCE ON
'CONSERVATION IN WALES' ORGANISED BY THE
NATURALISTS' TRUSTS IN WALES AND THE
NATURE CONSERVANCY

P. SCHOFIELD, M.A.

Nature Conservancy

A CONFERENCE ON 'CONSERVATION IN WALES', attended by over 230
people and organised jointly by the Naturalists' Trusts in Wales and
the Nature Conservancy, was held at the University College of Wales,
Aberystwyth, from Friday, 19th September, to Sunday, 21st September,
1969. The Conference was an exercise in public participation in the
planning and management of the countryside and was an early contribution from Wales, through the Countryside in 1970 Committee for
Wales, to European Conservation Year 1970.

The success of the Conference was due largely to the fact that a wide
cross-section of Welsh opinion took part. There were representatives
from several government departments, local authorities, voluntary
bodies and cultural organizations, as well as planners, agriculturalists,
naturalists and many private individuals.

Dr M. E. D. Poore, Director of the Nature Conservancy, opened
the programme on the Friday evening with a lively address which
was followed by a number of interesting questions. Dr Poore said
that future land use, including land for conservation, was a matter
of choice. However, would the choice of the present generation necessarily be the same or similar to that of future generations? We require
to know what possibilities are open to us and the full consequences of
the alternatives. It was essential that environmental and social scientists should make all aspects of land use clear so that those responsible
for taking decisions or influencing the course of events had the relevant facts before them. Dr Poore said that the conservationist aimed,
with ecological backing, to preserve land while still using it — to
have one's cake and to eat it, so to speak. The actions of this generation will not only affect the environment in our lifetime but will also

leave behind the effects for subsequent generations to cope with. While it is the responsibility of professionals to make others aware of the options, it is the responsibility of everyone not only to choose but to make choice effective. Whatever we choose, we must leave in the countryside a resilience which will provide for the future a range of alternative choices at least as wide as the one left for us.

Dr Poore concluded by saying that the function of a Conference such as this was to bring about by discussion a better understanding of the problems of land-use on the part of all those who manage and use the countryside. In this way also public participation in decision-making as to how land should be used could be increased and made more effective.

In answers to questions, Dr Poore stated that the roles of the Conservancy and the Naturalists' Trusts were closely linked. The Trusts could provide a complementary series of reserves and could focus public opinion on conservation matters. In relation to the Conservancy's priorities for choosing research topics, Dr Poore said the prospective projects were judged on the possible application of the results of research, particularly in relation to the practical management of plant and animal communities, on their addition to scientific knowledge and on their individual merits. Dr Poore was then asked how the Conservancy will 'preach to the unconverted'. Here he felt that the 'Countryside in 1970' exercise would be a great help; also the 'multiplier effect' from the converted, especially in schools, was of importance.

In the first session, on the Saturday morning, the Conference looked at 'The Planning Task'. This was then followed by sessions on 'Achievement and Trends', the 'Future Problems' and 'The Way Ahead'.

'The Planning Task' was introduced by Dr Margaret Davies, Chairman of the Countryside Commission in Wales. In this session Dr Tom Pritchard, Deputy Director of the Nature Conservancy in Wales, outlined the history of the development of the countryside in Wales and the future challenge to conservationists. The environment was being subjected to increasing pressures; demands upon its natural resources over the next few decades would be vastly in excess of anything we had experienced in the past. The higher standard of living, which we all expect, involving greater personal wealth and leisure, would result in greater requirements for water and minerals, higher productivity from the soil and seas, more land for housing, recreation and communication. As a result, the landscape would differ in several important respects from that which we know today. The landscape, however, has always been changing and providing the planners and users of land could develop new forms of land use and adopt certain ecological criteria, then future generations would not be expected to have lesser wealth of opportunity than we have today.

Mr Colin Cooper, Chief Planner, The Welsh Office, continued the theme, outlining some of the regional planning problems and changes which he thought might take place. Using the Vale of Glamorgan and other sites in South Wales as examples, Mr Cooper described some of the planning techniques which were being used to decide on the most suitable sites for new industry, communications network, towns and other developments which substantially affect the rural environment. Many questions were asked of Dr Pritchard and Mr Cooper concerning the conflicts of traditional and new forms of land use.

Under the chairmanship of Colonel H. Morrey Salmon the Conference then heard a survey of the achievements to date, and the role in the future of the voluntary and official bodies in maintaining the balance between conservation of the countryside and essential changes in the pattern of land use. As examples of the work being undertaken by the voluntary bodies, Mr A. E. Smith, of the Society for the Promotion of Nature Reserves, spoke about the County Naturalists' Trusts; Mr W. M. Condry spoke about the Royal Society for the Protection of Birds; Captain H. R. H. Vaughan about the Council for the Protection of Rural Wales and Mr J. H. Barrett about the National Trust. Mr Smith's introduction typified the spirit of the voluntary organisations when he stated 'One of the main purposes of E.C.Y. and, of course, of this Conference is to encourage people to participate in the conservation and improvement of the countryside. Whilst we still have a long way to go in this direction in Britain, our voluntary movement in the amenity and nature conservation fields offers a notable example to the rest of Europe. Our colleagues in the statutory bodies — scientists and administrators — will not mistake me if I emphasize the importance of the voluntary principle. We appreciate the vital importance of their role as, I am sure they do of ours. But it seems to me that what we make of the environment reflects our sense of values as a community just as much as the standards of our moral, social and political behaviour. Participation in the shaping of it is the surest way to a clearer understanding and a more intimate concern for its future.' Captain Vaughan took up the same theme when he said 'Since 1962, C.P.R.W. has continued to criticise and appeal against inappropriate, objectionable, and harmful developments but the main effort has been directed towards helping members and the public to become informed about the radical changes now occurring in land use. C.P.R.W. believes that in the circumstances of today, it is likely that the best protection for Rural Wales is public opinion which is well informed and as widely held as possible'. He went on to say 'The aims of C.P.R.W. are in the realm of the notional, the ideal and of the mind, rather than in the world of things and statistics. We believe that our most fruitful contribution to the maintenance of balance between conservation of the countryside and essential changes in land use is to help people to acquire a real comprehension of what is happening.'

On the Saturday evening, after an excursion to Devil's Bridge in the afternoon, Mr H. E. Evans, Welsh Secretary, Ministry of Agriculture, Fisheries and Food, chaired the Conference whilst a selection of the statutory bodies outlined their role. Mr Peter Walters Davies, of the Nature Conservancy, aroused considerable interest when he spoke of the review of nature reserves and potential reserves which was nearing completion. Following this review, an ecological evaluation and a map showing grades of environment had been produced. The importance of zones and corridors of scientific, natural history and general natural resource interest were clearly shown on these maps and it was hoped they would be able to play an important part in the overall planning of the Welsh countryside. Dr Margaret Davies, Chairman of the Countryside Commission's Committee for Wales, then outlined the history and development of the Countryside Acts, and of the Commission's achievements in the Principality. Some very useful information was given to the Conference in relation to grant aid available for country projects, thus clarifying considerably the present situation. Dr Davies went on to describe how, in 1972, to celebrate the centenary of Yellowstone, U.S.A., the first National Park in the World, the Commission hopes, after consultations with Local Authorities, both Farmers' Unions, the C.L.A. and the public, to designate a Cambrian Mountains National Park. This designation, if approved by the Secretary of State, would be in recognition of the beauty of the area which is the largely uninhabited mountain spine of Wales lying between the Dovey estuary and Talley. The Commission envisages few sophisticated facilities for tourists within the boundaries but believes that a Cambrian Mountains National Park could make a contribution to the growth of tourism in mid-Wales, especially in the small towns near to the Park. Mr D. W. Jones-Williams, talking about the work of the Local Authorities, said that their responsibilities, especially those of Local Planning Authorities, are heavier than those of national statutory or voluntary bodies, because they cannot be so single-minded. They have to balance the various interests and pressures on the environment. At Trawsfynydd, for example, they had to balance damage to environment against revitalizing the local economy and boosting the national economy. As a local government officer, he strongly recommended that the private individual took a keener interest in local affairs because it was only through such participation that the Planners could produce the best long-term schemes. Mr J. W. L. Zehetmayr, Senior Officer for Wales, Forestry Commission,

PLATE 12. Salmon returning to spawning grounds in the Afon Lledr, about halfway between Pont Lledr and the river's confluence with the Afon Conwy. This is the first obstacle which the fish have to jump in the Lledr after leaving the Conwy. Most rivers in North and mid-Wales are as yet unpolluted.

completed this session with a description of the Commission's activities and the future of forestry in Wales. In the Jubilee Year of the Commission, he spoke only briefly of its major functions as a timber producer and concentrated on the lesser but important responsibilities for conserving the natural beauty and amenity of the countryside and provision for public access and recreation.

On the Sunday the Conference was honoured by the presence of Mrs Eirene White, M.P., Minister of State for Wales, who had the difficult task of chairing the session on 'Future Problems'. In this session the Conference heard in outline some of the future requirements and demands on the environment from several of the potential major land users, thus developing in more detail the points in Dr Pritchard's first paper. Because of the size of the task the Conference split into five discussions groups. *Recreation*: Chairman, H. J. Hambury, F.R.C.S., Glamorgan County Naturalists' Trust; Leader, Cadfan Davies, T.D. (Sports Council for Wales). *Agriculture and Forestry*: Chairman, Harry Soan, Brecknock County Naturalists' Trust; Leader, Mr H. Edmunds (Deputy Director, N.A.A.S., Wales). *Water Conservation*: Chairman, J. L. Fox, Herefordshire and Radnorshire Nature Trust; Leader, Mr D. Edmonds (Regional Engineer for Wales, M.A.F.F.). *Industry*: Chairman, Ben Feaver, West Wales Naturalists' Trust; Leader, Mr S. C. Vowles (Manager, Fawley Refinery, Esso Petroleum Company). *Education and care of the countryside*: Chairman, W. S. Lacey, Ph.D., D.Sc., North Wales Naturalists' Trust; Leader, Mr Wynne Ll. Lloyd, C.B. (Chief Inspector of Schools, Wales). After group discussions the leaders opened a general discussion in the main lecture hall. It was largely as a result of the participation and discussion at this stage of the Conference that a Manifesto was produced in the final session. Mrs Eirene White, M.P., then spoke of the Welsh Office responsibilities concerning conservation, the planning of the physical environment and economic development. She went on to say that the Welsh Office was deeply concerned with the subject matter of the Conference and hoped that the Welsh Office could act as an 'honest broker' in the reconciliation of conflicting interests which were bound to occur in everyday life. The Minister then referred to the Welsh Office 'Land Use Strategy' which she saw as a three-fold problem: identification, communication and reconciliation. The Minister closed the session by saying how impressed she was by the many good ideas that had been put forward at the Conference, which augured well for progress in 1970.

Participation by members of the Conference was at its height in the last session, 'The Way Ahead'. Dr Pritchard summarised the environmental picture and suggested means of obtaining a co-ordinated approach to the planning, use and development of the countryside.

The conclusion and recommendations of the morning reports, having been provisionally arranged over a hectic lunch, were ruthlessly hammered into shape during the afternoon and agreement was reached on a twelve-point manifesto for Public Participation in Conservation for the '70's.

The Conference Organisers, Mr Dillwyn Miles, West Wales Naturalists' Trust and Mr P. Walters Davies, The Nature Conservancy; Mr Harry Soan whose suggestions for a meeting of naturalists led to the idea of the Conference; Mr Norman Young who arranged the excellent excursion from Aberystwyth to Devil's Bridge in the Vale of Rheidol (itself an example of public participation); all those who arranged exhibits; the secretaries and helpers; and particularly the Conference members themselves are to be congratulated on producing a stimulating weekend and a major contribution from Wales to European Conservation Year. The Organisers hope that the Conference has provided the foundations which will allow many more individuals and organizations to understand their environment a little more and will enable them to care for it with greater enthusiasm.

THE MANIFESTO

1. Public attention must be drawn to the need to save water.

2. Procedures for public participation need to be reviewed.

3. Planning consultation procedures need to be reviewed.

4. Liaison between industry and voluntary conservation bodies should be encouraged.

5. Education authorities should ensure that all school-leavers understand the basis of ecological principles.

6. A study of the environment potential in the educational process should be made with special regard to the provision of field studies and outdoor education.

7. Communication between ecologists, conservationists and other environmentalists and the practical farmer and forester should be stimulated, particularly through the medium of voluntary bodies.

8. Schemes which integrate agriculture, forestry, recreation and the conservation of wildlife should be developed.

9. The voluntary conservation movement should have better representation on the Sports Council for Wales.

10. Voluntary conservation bodies should encourage the perpetuation and extension of the present situation whereby access to much of the countryside is through the consent of landowners and farmers, and act positively to improve public behaviour in the countryside.

11. Members of voluntary conservation bodies should make more effort to take an active part in local authority affairs.

12. The voluntary conservation movement has an important role to play along with statutory bodies in the conservation of the environment and similar conferences should be held on a regular basis so that such co-operation and communication may be strengthened.

FURTHER READING

TOPOGRAPHICAL AND GEOLOGICAL

Howe, G. M. and Thomas, P. (1963), *Welsh Land Forms and Scenery*. MacMillan.

North, F. J., Campbell, B. and Scott, R. (1949), *Snowdonia*. Collins.

Pocock, R. W. and Whitehead, T. H. (1961), *British Regional Geology: The Welsh Borderland*. H.M.S.O.

Pringle, J. and George, T. N. (1961), *British Regional Geology: South Wales*. H.M.S.O.

Smith, B. and George, T. N. (1961), *British Regional Geology: North Wales*. H.M.S.O.

Stamp, L. Dudley (1946), *Britain's Structure and Scenery*. Collins.

Steers, J. A. (1946), *The Coastline of England and Wales*. C.U.P.

Steers, J. A. (1953), *The Sea Coast*. Collins.

Steers, J. A. (1960), *The Coastline of England and Wales in Pictures*. C.U.P.

BIOLOGICAL

Bardsey Bird and Field Reports (1953-1970), are predominantly ornithological but include a wide range of botanical and zoological articles.

Barrett, J. H. and Yonge, C. M. (1958), *Pocket Guide to the Sea Shore*. Collins.

Condry, W. M. (1966), *The Snowdonia National Park*. Collins.

Jones, W. E., Editor (1968), *Natural History of Anglesey*. Anglesey Antiquarian Society.

Lewis, J. R. (1964), *The Ecology of Rocky Shores*. E.U.P.

Lockley, R. M. (1938), *I know an Island*. Harrap. (Skokholm and Grassholm).

Lockley, R. M. (1950), *Island of Skomer*, Staples Press.

Lockley, R. M. (1969), *The Island*. Deutsch. (Skokholm).

North, F. J., Campbell, B. and Scott, R. (1949), *Snowdonia*. Collins.

Pearsall, W. H. (1950), *Mountains and Moorlands*. Collins.

Yonge, C. M. (1949), *The Sea Shore*. Collins.

The journal *Nature in Wales,* published jointly by the West Wales, North Wales, Brecknock County and Radnorshire Section of the Herefordshire and Radnorshire Trusts contains many interesting articles and field notes on the natural history of the whole of Wales.

BOTANICAL

Carter, P. W. (1955), Botanical Exploration in Merionethshire. *The Merioneth Miscellany.*

Carter, P. W. (1955), The Botany of the Breidden Hills. *Report of the Montgomeryshire Field Society.*

Gillham, M. E. (1953), An Ecological Account of the vegetation of Skokholm and Grassholm. *Journ. Ecol., vol. 41.*

Hepburn, I. (1952), *Flowers of the Coast.* Collins.

Lousley, J. E. (1950), *Wild Flowers of Chalk and Limestone.* Collins.

Raven, J. E. and Walters, S. M. (1956), *Mountain Flowers.* Collins.

Summerhayes, V. S. (1951), *Wild Orchids of Britain.* Collins.

Turner, S. R. (1970), *Potentilla rupestris* on Craig Breidden. *Countryside,* vol. 21, p. 255.

ZOOLOGICAL

Davis, P. and Jones, P. Hope (1969-1970), Welsh Bird Reports for 1968 and 1969. Published annually in *Nature in Wales.*

Fisher, J. and Lockley, R. M. (1954), *Sea Birds.* Collins.

Ford, E. B. (1945), *Butterflies.* Collins.

Heathcote, A., Griffin, D. and Salmon, H. M. (1967), The Birds of Glamorgan. *Proc. Cardiff Naturalists' Society.*

Ingram, C. G. S. and Salmon, H. M., revised Humphreys, P. N. (1963), The Birds of Monmouthshire.

Matheson, C. (1932), Changes in the Fauna of Wales in Historic Times.

Smith, S. G. (1948), The Butterflies and Moths found in the Counties of Flintshire, Denbighshire, Caernarvonshire, Anglesey and Merioneth. *Proc. Chester Soc. Nat. Sci.* Supplements in 1950, 1951 and 1954 include additions to the above and records for Montgomeryshire, Cardiganshire and Radnorshire.

South, R. (1961), *The Moths of the British Isles.* Warne. Wayside and Woodland Series. Other volumes in this series deal with beetles, dragonflies, grasshoppers etc.

Southern, H. N. (1964), *The Handbook of British Mammals.* Blackwell.

Van den Brink, F. H. (1967), *A Field Guide to the Mammals of Britain and Europe.* Collins.

GENERAL

Carr, H. R. C. and Lister, G. A. (1948), *The Mountains of Snowdonia.* Crosby Lockwood.

Condry, W. M. (1966), *The Snowdonia National Park.* Collins.

Davies, M. (1958), *Wales in Maps.* University of Wales Press.

Hilton, K. J. (1967), *The Lower Swansea Valley Project.* Longmans Green.

Hoskins, W. G. and Stamp, L. Dudley (1963), *The Common Lands of England and Wales.* Collins.

Mellanby, K. (1967), *Pesticides and Pollution.* Collins.

Nicholson, E. M. (1957), *Britain's Nature Reserves.* Country Life.

Stamp, L. Dudley (1955), *Man and the Land.* Collins.

Stamp, L. Dudley (1969), *Nature Conservation in Britain.* Collins. This book contains a very full bibliography on wildlife and conservation, including official documents and reports of official and other bodies, as well as more general works, scientific journals, atlases and maps.

Attention is drawn to the following bodies which publish Annual Reports and Guides with information relating to Wales.

Council for the Protection of Rural Wales. Annual Reports.

Field Studies Council. Annual Reports. *Field Studies* since 1959.

Forestry Commission. Annual Reports. National Forest Park Guides (e.g. *Snowdonia National Forest Park Guide, Camping in National Forest Parks*).

National Parks (now Countryside) Commission. Annual Reports. National Park Guides (e.g. *Snowdonia*).

National Trust. Annual Reports. List of Properties (revised from time to time).

Nature Conservancy. Annual Reports. Monographs (e.g. *Wildfowl in Britain*). Countryside in 1970 Conference Proceedings.

Wildfowlers' Association of Great Britain and Ireland. Annual Report and Yearbook.

APPENDIX I

PARTICIPATING ORGANIZATIONS

Brecknock County Naturalists' Trust.
Botanical Society of the British Isles (Welsh Region).
Countryside Commission (Welsh Committee).
Field Studies Council.
Forestry Commission.
Glamorgan County Naturalists' Trust.
Monmouthshire Naturalists' Trust.
National Trust.
Nature Conservancy.
North Wales Naturalists' Trust.
Radnorshire Section of Herefordshire and Radnorshire Nature Trust.
Royal Society for the Protection of Birds.
Society for the Promotion of Nature Reserves.
West Wales Naturalists' Trust.

SUPPORTING ORGANIZATIONS AND INDIVIDUALS

County Councils of Anglesey, Cardiganshire, Carmarthenshire, Denbighshire, Flintshire, Glamorgan, Monmouthshire, Merioneth, Montgomeryshire and Pembrokeshire.
H. J. Hambury, F.R.C.S., Glamorgan.
A. J. Pickering, F.G.S., Caernarvonshire.
A. E. Smith, Cheshire.

APPENDIX II

ADDRESSES OF ORGANIZATIONS WITH CONSERVATION INTERESTS IN WALES

The abbreviations are those used in Appendix III (Key to the Map).

The Royal Society for the Protection of Birds (R.S.P.B.):
The Director, The Lodge, Sandy, Bedfordshire.

The National Trust (N.T.):
North Wales — Dinas, Betws-y-coed, Caernarvonshire.
South Wales — Napier House, Spilman Street, Carmarthen.

The Society for the Promotion of Nature Reserves (S.P.N.R.):
The Manor House, Alford, Lincolnshire.

The Forestry Commission (F.C.):
North Wales — Victoria Terrace, Aberystwyth, Cardiganshire.
South Wales — Churchill House, Churchill Way, Cardiff.

The Field Studies Council (F.S.C.):
The Secretary, 9 Devereux Court, Strand, London, W.C.2.
(Field Centres at Dale Fort and Orielton in Pembrokeshire, and at
Rhyd-y-creuau, near Betws-y-coed, Caernarvonshire).

The Council for the Protection of Rural Wales (C.P.R.W.):
Meifod, Montgomeryshire.

The Nature Conservancy, part of the Natural Environment Research
Council (N.E.R.C.):
North Wales — Penrhos Road, Bangor, Caernarvonshire.
South Wales — Plas Gogerddan, Aberystwyth, Cardiganshire.

The Countryside Commission, formerly National Parks Commission
(N.P.):
Committee for Wales, 30 Highfields, Llandaff, Cardiff CF5 2QB.

The Glamorgan County Naturalists' Trust (G.C.N.T.):
Hon. General Secretary: Group Capt. E. F. Campbell-Smith, 12
Caswell Drive, Mumbles, Swansea.
(Branches based on Swansea, Cardiff, Merthyr Tydfil and Port
Talbot).

The West Wales Naturalists' Trust Ltd. (W.W.N.T.):
Hon. General Secretary: Dillwyn Miles, 4 Victoria Place, Haverfordwest, Pembrokeshire.
(Branches based on Haverfordwest, Tenby, Newport, Aberystwyth, Carmarthen and Dolgellau).

The Herefordshire and Radnorshire Nature Trust Ltd. (H.R.N.T.):
Hon. Secretary: R. H. Bennett, 25 Castle Street, Hereford.
(Branches in Hereford and Llandrindod Wells).

The North Wales Naturalists' Trust Ltd. (N.W.N.T.):
Hon. General Secretary: Dr. W. S. Lacey, School of Plant Biology, University College of North Wales, Bangor, Caernarvonshire.
Executive Officer: D. W. Shaw, Llys Gwynedd, Ffordd Gwynedd, Bangor, Caernarvonshire.
(Branches in Montgomeryshire; Flintshire and East Denbighshire; Conway Valley, Llandudno and Colwyn Bay Area; and Anglesey).

The Monmouthshire Naturalists' Trust Ltd. (M.N.T.):
Hon. Secretary: A. T. Sawyer, 40 Melbourne Way, Newport, Monmouthshire.

The Brecknock County Naturalists' Trust Ltd. (B.C.N.T.):
Hon. General Secretary: H. M. Budgen, Byddwn, Llanhamlach, Brecon.

The Botanical Society of the British Isles, Welsh Region (B.S.B.I.):
Tal Ebolion, Cilycwm, Llandovery, Carmarthenshire.

The Wildfowlers' Association of Great Britain and Ireland.
Grosvenor House, 104 Watergate Street, Chester.

APPENDIX III

KEY TO THE MAP SHOWING LOCATION OF NATURE RESERVES, WILDFOWL REFUGES, BIRD SANCTUARIES, AND BIRD OBSERVATORIES IN WALES

Notes: 1. The Map and Key give the situation early in 1970.

2. Hedgerow and Roadside Nature Reserves are not included.

3. In those Nature Reserves established on National Trust properties where public rights of way exist access along footpaths is possible without permit, but for access to areas away from public footpaths permission must be obtained from the Management Authority.

4. Many of the Nature Reserves have been established on private property: on some breeding birds have to be protected from disturbance. Visitors must contact the Management Authority before entering.

Number	Name	Management Authority	Grid Reference
ANGLESEY			
1.	Cemlyn Lagoon	N.T./N.W.N.T.	SH 3393
2.	Cors Erddreiniog	N.E.R.C.	SH 4781
3.	Cors Goch	N.W.N.T.	SH 5081
3a.	Ynys Seiriol (Puffin Island) Bird Sanctuary	Baron Hill Estate	SH 6582
4.	Craig Wen	N.W.N.T.	SH 4980
5.	Newborough Warren and Ynys Llanddwyn	N.E.R.C.	SH 4065
BRECON			
6.	Cilhepste Coed	Univ. Coll. Swansea	SN 9209
7.	Craig Cerrig Gleisiad	N.E.R.C.	SN 8454
8.	Craig y Cilau	N.E.R.C.	SO 1815
9.	Craig y Rhiwarth	B.C.N.T.	SN 8415
10.	Cwm Clydach	N.E.R.C.	SO 2112
12.	Nant Irfon	N.E.R.C.	SM 8454
13.	Penmoelallt	N.E.R.C.	SO 0109
14.	Ty-mawr Pool	B.C.N.T.	SO 0726

Number	Name	Management Authority	Grid Reference
CAERNARVON			
15.	Coed Dolgarrog	N.E.R.C.	SH 7766
16.	Coed Gorswen	N.E.R.C.	SH 7570
17.	Coed Tremadoc	N.E.R.C.	SH 5841
18.	Cwm Glas Crafnant	N.E.R.C.	SH 7360
19.	Cwm Idwal	N.E.R.C.	SH 6459
20.	Gwydyr Bog	N.W.N.T.	SH 7659
21.	Morfa Bychan	N.W.N.T.	SH 5436
22.	Nantporth Quarry	N.W.N.T.	SH 5672
23.	Y Wyddfa — Snowdon	N.E.R.C.	SH 6054
	Bardsey Bird Observatory	Bardsey Bird and Field Observatory Council	SH 1222
CARDIGAN			
24.	Allt Crug Garn	W.W.N.T.	SN 5161
25.	Cardigan Island	W.W.N.T.	SN 1615
26.	Coed Rheidol	N.E.R.C.	SN 7478
27.	Cors Fochno	W.W.N.T.	SN 6391
28.	Cors Tregaron	N.E.R.C.	SN 6964
29.	Dyfi	N.E.R.C.	SN 6195
30.	Penderi Cliffs	W.W.N.T.	SN 5573
31.	Rhostie Bog	W.W.N.T.	SN 6173
32.	Teifi Valley and Foreshore (two reserves)	W.W.N.T.	SN 1846
33.	Ynyshir	R.S.P.B.	SN 6796
CARMARTHEN			
34.	Allt Rhyd y Groes	N.E.R.C.	SN 7647
35.	Nant Melin	W.W.N.T.	SN 7246
36.	Y Goyallt	W.W.N.T.	SN 7844
11.	Gwenffrwd	R.S.P.B.	SN 7546
DENBIGH			
37.	Cilygroeslwyd Wood	N.W.N.T.	SJ 1255
FLINT			
38.	Ddol Marl Pit	N.W.N.T.	SJ 1471

Number	Name	Management Authority	Grid Reference
GLAMORGAN			
39.	Abergelli Wood	G.C.N.T.	SS 6402
40.	Berry Wood	G.C.N.T.	SS 4788
41.	Bolgoed Quarry	G.C.N.T.	SO 6002
42.	Broad Pool	G.C.N.T.	SS 5191
43.	Castle Wood Field	G.C.N.T.	SS 4793
44.	Coed Cefn Pwll Du	G.C.N.T./F.C.	ST 2187
45.	Coed y Bedw	G.C.N.T./F.C.	ST 1182
46.	Craig y Llyn	G.C.N.T./F.C.	SO 9003
47.	Cwm George	G.C.N.T./F.C.	ST 1472
48.	Cwm Ivy Wood (Pt).	G.C.N.T.	SS 4493
49.	Cwm Leyshon	G.C.N.T.	ST 2187
50.	Eglwys Nunydd Reservoir	G.C.N.T.	SS 8084
51.	Gelli-hir Wood	G.C.N.T.	SS 5692
52.	Glamorganshire Canal	Cardiff City Council.	ST 1480
53.	Gower Coast (Bird Sanctuary)	N.T./N.E.R.C.	SS 3987
	Burry Estuary National Wilfowl Refuge	⎫ N.T.	SS 4697
	Burry Holms-Twlc Point Bird Sanctuary	⎬ enquiries to	SS 4093
	Swansea Bay Bird Sanctuary	⎭ N.E.R.C.	SS 6290
54.	Ilston Quarry	G.C.N.T.	SS 5590
55.	Lavernock Point	G.C.N.T.	ST 1868
56.	Llanrhidion Hill	G.C.N.T.	SS 4992
57.	Melin Llan Wood	G.C.N.T.	SS 6299
58.	Ogmore Down	G.C.N.T.	SS.8976
59.	Oxwich	N.E.R.C.	SS 5087
60.	Peel Wood	G.C.N.T.	SS 6088
61.	Port Eynon and Overton	G.C.N.T.	SS.4684
62.	Ridgewood Park	G.C.N.T.	SS 6090
63.	Sedgers Bank	G.C.N.T.	SS 4784
64.	Whiteford	N.T./G.C.N.T./ N.E.R.C.	SS 4495
MERIONETH			
65.	Abercorris	W.W.N.T.	SH 7508
66.	Cader Idris	N.E.R.C.	SH 7112
67.	Coed Camlyn	N.E.R.C.	SH 6539
68.	Coed Cymerau	N.E.R.C.	SH 6842
69.	Coed Ganllwyd	N.E.R.C.	SH 7224
70.	Coed y Rhygen	N.E.R.C.	SH 6836

Number	Name	Management Authority	Grid Reference
71.	Cors y Sarnau	W.W.N.T.	SH 9739
72.	Maentwrog Woods	N.T./N.W.N.T./ N.E.R.C.	SH 6540
73.	Morfa Dyffryn	N.E.R.C.	SH 5625
74.	Morfa Harlech	N.E.R.C.	SH 5634
75.	Rhinog	N.E.R.C.	SH 6529

MONMOUTH

76.	Blackcliff and Wyndcliff	N.E.R.C./F.C.	ST 5397
77.	Cleddon Falls	M.N.T.	SO 5203
78.	Cwmbran Canal	M.N.T.	ST 2997
79.	Llanishen	M.N.T.	SO 4703
80.	Magor	M.N.T.	ST 4286
81.	Peterstone	M.N.T.	ST 2780
	Newport Bird Sanctuary	Newport County Borough Council	ST 3187

MONTGOMERY

82.	Breidden Hill (part)	N.W.N.T.	SJ 2814
83.	(under negotiation)	N.W.N.T.	————

PEMBROKE

84.	Grassholm Island	R.S.P.B./W.W.N.T.	SM 5909
85.	Llannerch Wood	W.W.N.T.	SN 0535
86.	Marloes Mere	W.W.N.T.	SM 7708
87.	Martin's Haven	W.W.N.T.	SM 7608
88.	Nevern Valley	W.W.N.T.	SN 1039
89.	Ramsey Island	R.S.P.B.	SM 7023
90.	St. Margaret's Island	W.W.N.T.	SN 1297
91.	Skokholm Island (Bird Observatory)	W.W.N.T.	SM 7305
92.	Skomer Island	W.W.N.T./N.E.R.C.	SM 7209
93.	West Hook Cliffs	W.W.N.T.	SM 7609

RADNOR

94.	Barns and Blue Links	H.R.N.T./F.C.	SO 0582

INDEX